THE THINKING MACHINE

Q

C D E F G H I J

A B C D E F

THE
THINKING
MACHINE

by John Pfeiffer

J·B·LIPPINCOTT COMPANY

Philadelphia & New York

ACKNOWLEDGMENTS

ONE OF THE MOST SIGNIFICANT DEVELOPMENTS in science is the rise of general-purpose electronic computers during the second half of the twentieth century. These large and complicated machines are being used to an increasing extent in practically every area of human endeavor: in government and industry, in the design of superhighways and jet planes and military devices, in many fields of medicine and basic research. Since the machines do things which could once be performed only by the human brain, it is inevitable that they should be compared with the brain and stimulate new investigations into the organization and function of man's nervous system.

This book is an introduction to the workings, accomplishments, and future possibilities of these rapidly evolving computers. It is based on "The Thinking Machine," a one-hour television program presented on October 26, 1960, on the CBS Television Network and sponsored by the American Machine and Foundry Company. The program is one of the "Tomorrow" series produced by the Public Affairs Department of CBS News in cooperation with the Massachusetts Institute of Technology as part of the Institute's Centennial celebrations. It is unusual in a number of respects. For one thing, it focuses attention on advances which are already affecting our ways of living and thinking. For another, it represents a high point in efforts to bring science to mass audiences of nonscientists.

The book would have been impossible without the active help of many investigators who gave generously of their time in describing their current studies and plans for the future. The following is a list of those I spoke with at M.I.T.: Dean Arden, Wesley Clark, Fernando Corbato, Jack Dennis, Heinrich Ernst, Belmont Farley, Jay Forrester, Frederick Frick, Bert Green, Jerome Lettvin, Arthur Loeb, John McCarthy, Warren McCulloch, Charles Miller, Marvin Minsky, Harrison Morse, Philip Morse, William Papian, Ithiel Pool, Robert Price, Lawrence Roberts, Walter Rosenblith, Douglas T. Ross, Oliver Selfridge, Claude Shannon, Victor Starr, Herbert Taeger, and Victor Yngve.

Although the book leans heavily on studies under way at M.I.T., it also draws on considerable research being done elsewhere. I have received important help from Alex Bernstein of the Simulmatics Corporation, New York; Grace Hopper, Malcolm Smith, and Todd Williams of Remington Rand Univac; Edward Lasker, New York chess master; Lawrence Riddle and Richard Brady of the Burroughs Corporation; Herbert Simon of the Carnegie Institute of Technology; Sam Ulam and Mark Wells of the Los Alamos Scientific Laboratory; Truman Hunter, Herman Goldstine, and Arthur Samuel of International Business Machines Corporation; Gabe Sellers of the Bell Telephone Laboratories; John Gilmore of Charles W. Adams Associates in Bedford, Mass.; John Diebold of John Diebold & Associates; and James McDonough of Concord Control Inc. in Boston.

I want to acknowledge my debt to Murray Benson of CBS, and to Thomas H. Wolf of CBS, writer-producer of the television version of "The Thinking Machine." Because of his complete cooperation I had access to the extensive files of notes and publications which he and his co-workers gathered during preparatory research at M.I.T. and other institutions. Finally, I am also in debt to John Mattill, director of M.I.T.'s Office of Publications, who—in the midst of a schedule already jammed with Centennial as well as regular business—furnished invaluable help in putting me in touch with scientists and seeing to it that they received preliminary chapters for checking.

JOHN PFEIFFER

CONTENTS

ILLUSTRATIONS

THE THINKING MACHINE

CHAPTER 1

A NEW BREED OF MACHINES

O NE OF THE MOST UNUSUAL MACHINES of our times is working efficiently at the Massachusetts Institute of Technology, the birthplace of many unusual machines. It is housed on the second floor of the Research Laboratory of Electronics, in Room 26-248. As you enter the room, you see an array of upright steel panels, electronic mosaics of a sort built up of a large number of basic circuit units. These units are special "packets" plugged into panel sockets, each a compact transistor-containing circuit enclosed in transparent plastic sheets and about the size of a miniature radio set.

An investigator sits at a table near the panels. To his right is an electric typewriter, to his left a so-called "cathode-ray tube" with its television-type screen. The devices are part of a communication system between man and machine. In this particular study such a typewriter has fed raw experimental data and instructions into the mach'ne, which then followed the instructions and analyzed the data. It displays its results in the form of graphs, blue curved lines traced on the fluorescent screen. From time to time the investigator turns to the typewriter and, by pressing appropriate keys, records information for future displays.

As far as a casual inspection goes, that is about it. This is no Buck Rogers world-of-tomorrow laboratory, no display room dressed up to overawe impressionable visitors. A Hollywood producer in search of material for a cinematic spectacular would hardly choose it to illustrate his notions about what goes on in the wonderful world of science. If you want to see glamorous gadgetry and flashing lights and things that move in mysterious ways, if you want to hear strange hissing and cranking noises, you will have to go elsewhere. There is far more dramatic equipment than electronic computers at M.I.T. and at any other leading research center.

The machine in Room 26-248 may not be photogenic, but it has some commendable qualities. It is built to do a job and does it effectively, without benefit of fanfare or fancy interior decorating. Known as the TX-0 computer, it was built as part of an advanced computer-research program being carried out at the Institute's Lincoln Laboratory. It operates an average of 110 to 120 hours a week on an entirely routine basis. The last man to leave the room at the end of the day simply pushes the OFF button and goes home. The TX-0 and other general-purpose electronic calculating machines are used to help deal with a variety of highly complex problems in practically every major branch of science and technology—astronomy, nuclear physics, chemistry, weather forecasts, aircraft and missile design, and so on. They are also used in a wide range of business and social applications, from handling insurance records and predicting sales to traffic control and the analysis of voting returns.

This book is devoted to machines like the TX-0: large, general-purpose electronic computers which perform high-speed calculations by counting techniques. They are known as "digital" computers. They have been made possible by mass-production developments in the electronics industry,

M.I.T.'s Lincoln Laboratory—a leading center in the rapidly expanding area of computer research and technology. Birthplace of the TX-o computer.

developments which in the words of one scientist permit "the attainment of reliable complexity." They are a result of studies whose beginnings may be traced back to the work of Leibnitz and Pascal in the seventeenth and eighteenth centuries.

There are also other kinds of calculating machines. One important class includes "analog" computers, which do not deal with numbers as such. Instead, they turn numbers into something which may vary continuously, such as the speed of a rotating shaft or the flow of an electric current. Mechanical versions of such machines, so-called differential analyzers, were brought to a high stage of development more than thirty years ago by Vannevar Bush and his associates at M.I.T.

Digital computers are more precise than the analog variety. Furthermore, when it comes to individual calculations, they are faster. But when a problem exceeds a certain complexity, the digital computer may be called on to perform so many calculations that the time required to solve a problem is increased enormously. In fact, a number of important problems are far too time-consuming for the best of modern digital computers. In such cases the analog computer comes into its own. In a sense, it can handle the problem as a whole rather than as an appallingly long series of arithmetic steps. But we shall concentrate on digital, general-purpose computers, mainly because they are the machines being used in most of the exciting work under way at present.

The development of all sorts of computers comes at a crucial time. Indeed, it is difficult to imagine how we could cope with our problems if such computers did not exist. For one thing, science would be a less attractive profession. Investigators would find themselves spending more and more of their time wading through mountains of data and involved in the drudgery of repetitious calculations. The pace of scientific advance would slow down appreciably. The situation is difficult enough right now, even with computers. We are in the midst of an "information explosion" which already threatens to overwhelm us and is certain to become a matter of increasing concern during the years ahead.

The plain fact is that knowledge is growing at a prodigious rate. We are learning so much so swiftly that, without learning aids, we have neither the time nor the brainpower to keep up with the results of our own experiments. This state of affairs has been building up for a long while; only the magnitude of the problem is new. During ancient times relatively few people studied natural phenomena, and knowledge accumulated slowly. (Incidentally, there was top-secret information even in those days, and not only military information. Nearly two thousand years ago a Greek writer described how science could help produce "bewilderment and awe"—for instance, the power of expanding hot air was used in temples to open doors and move statues of gods.) In eighteenth-century Europe science, like polo and yachting today, was still largely an activity of gentlemen with ample personal funds and leisure.

Since then science and technology have become the full-time occupations of millions of persons. Furthermore, every investigator probably gathers more data in a week than his predecessors of a century or two ago gathered in months or years. He has at his service machines which are less widely publicized than the new computers, but which have played a major role in practically forcing the computers into existence. These machines are detectors and measuring devices, gluttons for information automatically grinding out masses of records. You can find them everywhere, in every laboratory.

Consider the output of one such device at the University of California's Radiation Laboratory. Nuclear physicists have developed a number of techniques for observing elusive subatomic particles which may endure less than a thousandth of a trillionth of a second before vanishing in bursts of pure energy. One technique involves the so-called "bubble chamber." When particles pass through certain liquids, they leave trails of bubbles such as may be seen in the wake of an underwater torpedo. A bubble chamber at the Radiation Laboratory contains liquid hydrogen and includes automatic cameras to record bubble-trail patterns. For more than two years these cameras have been taking snapshots at the rate of 10,000 a day.

Weather studies also call for enormous quantities of data. A network of some three hundred stations provides observations of upper-atmosphere air masses over the Northern Hemisphere. Twice a day each station receives radio messages transmitted from instruments in balloons drifting at various altitudes up to about 100,000 feet. The messages provide measurements of temperature, wind velocity, wind direction, humidity, and so on. Other Northern Hemisphere stations receive wind data only. The result is a total of about forty-five thousand numbers a day, a small part of the flood of more than half a million numbers which flow daily into the Weather Bureau's Washington headquarters.

Another example, this one from the field of medical research: Groups of nerve cells in the brain continually fire in unison; that is, they emit rhythmical pulses of electricity, or brain waves. The pulses can be recorded by attaching electrical contacts to the scalp and running wires from the contacts to a special measuring device known as an electroencephalograph or EEG machine. Automatic pens write signatures of nerve-cell rhythms in the form of brain-wave charts, patterns of wavy lines on moving chart paper which doctors use to study normal and abnormal activities of the brain. There are hundreds of brain-wave laboratories in medical centers throughout the nation. At one of them, located in Columbia University's College of Physicians and Surgeons, EEG machines turn out nearly five miles of brain-wave charts every week.

There is no stopping this flood, although some people have wistfully considered the idea. We live in an expanding universe of information. Scientific data accumulate in roll after roll of charts obtained from studies of starlight on Palomar Mountain, in the 4 million depth soundings made by oceanographers every month as they map undersea topography—and in the collected observations of about thirty thousand investigators working at thousands of stations during the International Geophysical Year. It is a serious problem merely to store the swelling records of current research, merely to put them in out-of-the-way places where they will not clutter up valuable working space.

Studying even a fraction of the data represents a still more formidable problem. Of course, in theory at least, one solution is always available. Several years ago I visited a British laboratory designed especially for research on meteor orbits. Every time a meteor passed within the range of scanning radar stations, day or night, a pair of green dots flashed on the screen of a cathode-ray tube and a camera recorded the event on film.

The investigator in charge of the apparatus told me that it provided from 2,000 to 3,500 photographs a week, each photograph including sufficient data to plot the orbit of one meteor. He added that the job of translating one week of records into meteor orbits required nearly a full year of paper work. I asked him how the laboratory managed to keep up with the machine: "We don't. We shut the machine off. Most of the time it's not operating."

While such a strategy may relieve the pressure somewhat in certain cases, it could hardly serve as a basis for international policy in science. We cannot expect investigators the world over to declare an official moratorium on all varieties of data collecting, and pull out the plugs connecting laboratory instruments to their power supplies. The urge to learn is too deep-rooted for that, and in the absence of an inspection system someone would be sure to make observations on the sly. Besides, the fruits of learning are too valuable.

A more palatable and practical alternative is to call on the large electronic computer for help, which is just what is happening. The demand has increased markedly during the past decade. In 1950, a dim and distant past considering how swiftly science moves, the United States had less than half a dozen such machines in regular operation. Today we have about seven hundred, which is roughly twice as many as the rest of the world combined. Design and construction budgets are high. It costs from $500,000 to $10,000,000 and up to build one of these machines. They are not luxuries, however. They are among the most expensive necessities yet invented. As a general rule, they are not sold but rented at rates as high as $350 to more than $600 an hour.

Although that may appear to be a steep price, it is less than the earnings of some businessmen and motion-picture stars. Moreover, you have to take into account the amount of work a computer does. One computer, a fast model but not the fastest, can calculate about 175,000 times faster than a man using a desk-type adding machine. In other words, it performs as many arithmetic operations in a single hour as the man could perform in twenty years. Considering that rate of production, hourly rentals seem more reasonable and the machines more than pay their way.

Some statistics may indicate another reason why science will depend to a greater and greater extent on the supply of high-speed computers. According to an estimate made last year, the world's publishers every year turn out some 75,000 weekly and monthly research journals as well as 60,000 scientific books. If we add the material appearing in special reports, monographs, and other publications, the annual total comes to about sixty million pages of technical literature. Another estimate expresses the same general point in different terms: the sum of human knowledge doubles every ten or fifteen years. It is no wonder that the scientist cannot begin to keep up with all current developments, even when he confines himself to work in his own specialized field.

A result of the rapid pile-up of information is that experimental findings, some of them extremely important, may be lost in the shuffle. Material may be published and never come to the notice of investigators who could use it in their work. So there is a certain tendency to do things that have been done before, to go around in circles covering the same old ground. In a recent discussion one Nobel Prize winner suggested that, if the trend continued and nothing were done about it, the future might see "all but the most outstanding discoveries" being repeated every thirty years or so.

Such duplication of effort may be relatively rare at present, or it may be more common than many scientists suspect. We have no way of knowing precisely. But the tendency is a dangerous one. It amounts to a blockage of communications, and as long as we lack adequate countermeasures, science is sure to suffer in the long run. Indeed, this blockage produces the same effects as military or industrial secrecy, the chief difference being that it is not of our own choosing.

Part of the trouble has to do with the language barrier. Some information is undoubtedly lost because it has not been translated. From the standpoint of the United States and other English-speaking nations, things may become more serious in the years ahead, particularly as large countries like India and China contribute more and more to international research. In the past we have been slow to appreciate the full importance of learning foreign languages. For every American scientist who reads Russian, for example, there are about five hundred Russian scientists who read English. Although figures are not available, there can be little doubt that the ratio is even more unfavorable to us when it comes to comparisons involving Japanese or Chinese scientists.

A basic approach to this aspect of the problem, of course,

is wider and improved education in languages. Electronic computers may also help, and considerable work is under way in an effort to develop machines capable of preparing reasonably sophisticated translations. (This work, by the way, is proving rather more difficult than some of the headlines would indicate.) On the other hand, education and machine translation will never be sufficient by themselves. Before you can translate an article, you must find it—and that means that it or a good abstract must first be brought to the attention of interested investigators. In other words, that places the responsibility directly on the persons who organize our great storehouses of information, our libraries.

Incomplete bibliographies often result in wasted effort. Even such a relatively minor oversight as failing to include one reference in a long list of references may delay the progress of important research projects. For example, in 1950 engineers at several American companies were concerned with an extremely complicated problem in the design of electrical circuits. They searched through the scientific literature to learn whether the problem had been solved by other workers and, finding no evidence that it had, launched a special study of their own. Five years later the problem was still unsolved, at least as far as the American engineers were concerned. But someone else happened to have done the fundamental work that would have led to a quick solution if his work had been available at the right time.

In 1950, the same year that the engineers started their research, a Russian scientist reported this work in the *Journal of the U.S.S.R. Academy of Sciences.* Furthermore, a fifteen-line abstract of the article was published by the editors of *Mathematical Reviews,* also during 1950. Yet the Russian report remained buried until it was finally discovered in 1955. By that time five years of fruitless work had cost the American companies at least $200,000. Information is a valuable commodity. We pay a high price when it comes too late or not at all.

This is just a single example of the sort of situation confronting investigators of all nations actively conducting research. What can we do about it? For one thing, a new profession has been created in many industrial research organizations. There are scientifically skilled specialists who do not fit into either the researcher or the administrator category. Their job is to keep themselves up to date on reports in various fields of science, and to pass the facts on to investigators in the laboratory. They are middlemen of a unique kind, directing the flow and distribution of information at a high level. They generally earn their salaries many times over.

Efficient use of information also demands more trained librarians. But it is not enough merely to enlarge the staffs of technical libraries. Many of the operations required in indexing, cross-indexing, and filing and retrieving information are sheer routines, mental assembly-line work. Here, again, we are beginning to call on machines. Computers are being used increasingly to help prepare indexes at speeds far exceeding the capabilities of human workers. In any case, and this is the big point, we will soon need radically new ways of preparing technical literature. Right now it is addressed primarily to scientists and engineers. Before long it will also have to be presented in a form which machines can read and index and abstract automatically. We shall have more to say in a later chapter about special languages for communicating with machines.

Broadly speaking, the development of large high-speed computers is a direct consequence of the rapid growth of science. There is a kind of logic in this development. Man is a limited species in many ways and much of his thinking has been concentrated on overcoming his limitations. He has invented devices to extend his senses, artificial sense organs. With the aid of telescopes and suitable photographic film he can observe events taking place 6 billion light-years away, perhaps near the very edge of the expanding universe. In the microcosmic world he sees the detailed structure of simple self-reproducing things, viruses some of which are so small that billions of them could fit comfortably in a sphere no bigger across than the period at the end of this sentence. Electronic amplifiers can convert the sound of a beetle scuttling through the grass into a noise as loud as an army marching in step.

We create new senses as well as extend the power of natural senses. We have no sense organs designed to detect magnetism, but devices sensitive to magnetic fields help us prospect for buried mineral deposits and study geological changes miles below the surface of the ocean. Our eyes are not designed to detect radio waves, but radio telescopes pick up static from the depths of space and reveal the existence of "radio stars," remote broadcasting centers many of which cannot be observed by our most powerful optical telescopes. We have focused radio telescopes on nearby stars presumed to have planets in a search, unsuccessful as yet, for signals from other creatures at least as advanced as we are.

The information which threatens to swamp us now comes largely from these artificial sense organs and the automatic recorders attached to them. The next step is inevitable. Having extended and multiplied our senses and thereby enlarged our universe tremendously, we naturally should build machines to deal with the rising flood of information and help us analyze phenomena in our new universe. Artificial sense organs lead to artificial brains, and it would be strange indeed if we had one without the other. Arguments that computers do not *actually* think miss the essential point, tend to be oversubtle, and are already becoming academic and just a bit dated.

Of course computers think. (Another problem—are brains computing machines?—is something else again and we shall come to it later.) They do for the brain what other machines do for the muscles. We hear no arguments as to whether or not bulldozers *actually* do work, and you can say they do work without worrying about ruffled feelings or without having to defend your position. No one is going to stand up and challenge you to define what you mean by "work." Bulldozers gouge and butt their way through masses of earth, and if you ever have a chance to try running one yourself, you will quickly appreciate that the job depends very much on the skill of the man at the controls. In countries where bulldozers are scarce men do the same sort of work with picks and shovels, sometimes with their hands. People can be used to accomplish anything that a bulldozer can accomplish, and a great deal more. But such points have nothing whatever to do with the bare fact that bulldozers work.

And in the same basic sense, computers think. They include devices which store information and units designed to perform elementary arithmetic and logical operations. Other units control long sequences of individual steps and determine when information is to be extracted from or put into memory devices. Without investigators to prepare problems, to tell them what to do, computers are as inert and useless as a bulldozer without an operator. People with abacuses and adding machines are doing the sort of thinking that more advanced computers do—and it should go without saying that there are types of thinking beyond the powers of any existing computer. If we want to define thinking in some way that would exclude the activities of computers, we are certainly free to do so. We can also define working in such a way that bulldozers would be excluded. But in both cases, aside from the pleasure of playing with words, the effort seems rather pointless.

Man-made thinking machines, like the begotten variety, are used for purposes other than research in the physical and biological sciences. So far we have discussed problems related chiefly to laboratory findings and the accumulation of experimental data. But *everything* is becoming more complicated, not just science. It has long been more or less true that events in one part of the world influence other parts. Today, however, the effects are felt more rapidly and produce more persistent and widespread disturbances than ever before. Societies and nations are "tightly coupled," in the sense that actions tend to bring about sharp and prompt reactions. This is part of what we mean by saying that rapid transportation and communications have made the world smaller.

An analogy may help emphasize the difference between the world of the twentieth century and the good old days, between tightly and loosely coupled systems. Most of the time we get along by playing the odds. We spend an appreciable proportion of our lives acting in good faith on an assumption that is not entirely without risk—namely that what was will continue to be, that the past in all likelihood provides reliable clues to what will happen in the future. We go by probabilities instinctively; the tendency seems to be built into us.

The occurrence of a surprise often signifies that something has gone wrong. A hundred years ago a man at the reins of a horse and buggy usually had time to detect and meet road emergencies. He moved slowly enough so that he could see a fallen tree or some other obstacle on the road ahead and stop before having a collision. Handling a car is another matter. A driver negotiating a low-visibility curve depends more critically upon the odds. He tends to assume a conventional future: the road ahead, like the road behind, will be free of obstacles. Any surprise, a stalled car or a dog loping across the road, may mean catastrophe. More often than not, but not always, the driver has time to readjust his expectations and avoid trouble. Now consider a higher order of speed. By the time a pilot in a fast jet plane sees another plane in his path, it is already too late to steer out of a collision. If the pilot depends solely on his brain and nervous system to avoid such situations, if his only guide is the assumption that the future will be like the past, he is a dead man.

We are living in a transition time between automobile and jet worlds. As a rule, the effect of an error in judgment is less obvious and less spectacular than a head-on collision. But the basic principle is the same. Acting in time is more crucial than ever, whether it involves the policies of a company or a government or the United Nations. Decisions must be made, and made quickly. Furthermore, they had better be the right decisions. In many situations mistakes are becoming increasingly irrevocable. Yet in a more and more complex world it is more difficult to arrive at an adequate basis for action.

There may be ways out of this apparent impasse. When the brain falters or fails in its efforts to arrive at valid decisions, the computer can offer invaluable assistance. Take a military problem, for example. Bismarck was not thinking about computers when he said that war is too important to be left to generals. But his remark may be interpreted in a new sense today. During World War II it became obvious that a modern battle is a phenomenon so intricate that neither generals nor any other specialists can devise effective strategies solely on the basis of experience and intuition. Decision-making requires a complete presentation of the facts, or at least a reasonably complete presentation. But it is often impossible for human beings without computers to get the facts, organize them, and use them to determine effective action—all at a high rate of speed.

Certain defense problems are a case in point. To protect the United States and its outposts against attacks, the Air Force needs a bewildering variety of information. In the first place, it must know the present position, speed, altitude, and flight direction of every single one of the airplanes aloft in a vast area. It must keep track of all the planes, maintaining a continuous record of their courses and changing positions. It must have the daily flight plans of all military, commercial, and private planes—so that unscheduled planes can be spotted promptly. Then it must have some way of distinguishing friend from foe. If enemy planes are approaching, they must be counted and followed —and met with interceptor planes or missiles or antiaircraft guns or some combination thereof.

No team of scientists and military experts could perform all these duties fast enough to keep pace with the speeds of modern planes. The work is done by a special Air Force system known as SAGE (for Semi-Automatic Ground Environment, whatever *that* means). SAGE was designed by the Lincoln Laboratory of M.I.T., which also designed the TX-o computer, and includes a widespread network of radar stations to detect and follow aircraft. Groups of stations transmit a steady barrage of signals to regional centers where machines do what human beings cannot do. Computers take over the enormously complex job of making sense of the data.

If it ever comes to actual warfare, computers will have to be mobilized by the tens of thousands. The air over a battlefield is buzzing with information as well as more tangible flying things. Army scientists estimate that in an area of about sixty square miles our ground troops would be using at least 20,000 electronic devices. Each device would be emitting signals, and this does not include the signals of Navy and Air Force equipment. Only computers can coordinate on-the-spot battle activities, and they would be important targets for the enemy. If one of them were destroyed, the result might be a chaotic informational traffic jam.

Everything we have said about warfare applies with equal force to business. Most of the publicity about the feats of computers in large companies involves sorting, classifying, record-keeping, and similar duties. For example, most airlines have central computers for storing complete information on the availability of seats on all flights. When you ask for space at a local office, the clerk uses a push-button-switch device to communicate with the computer, and an answer comes back in about three seconds, which, incidentally, is considerably faster than the time it takes to write out your ticket. You will find computers wherever masses of information must be handled by methods that require the same steps over and over again. They are doing the dirty work, the routines and drudgery of day-to-day operations.

Such chores by no means exhaust the potentialities of computers. Machines can help us deal with complex as well as straightforward problems, tactics and strategies as well as routines. Although they serve mainly as electronic workhorses at the lower levels of the industrial hierarchy, they are coming up in the world. They may never replace vice presidents, presidents, and board chairmen—or even a good secretary. But executives are beginning to realize that computers, or rather the combination of computers and men trained to use them, can play a significant role in the shaping of policy. And it is at the policy-making level that the resemblances between business and warfare are most intriguing.

Certain basic principles hold for both areas. As a matter of fact, investigators experienced in designing computers and computer systems for military purposes are among the leaders concerned with new ways of tackling some of management's biggest problems. In business as in warfare, decisions must be made faster than ever in the face of conditions which are more complex and change more rapidly than ever. In business as in warfare, the advance of science and technology demands a degree of executive flexibility inconceivable to men who lived—or behave as if they were still living—in less hectic times. (Many companies make most of their current profits from the sale of products which did not exist a decade or so ago.)

Of course, there are important differences. Generally speaking, top-level business problems are at least an order of magnitude more complex than top-level military problems. Objectives in industry tend to be less clearly and less precisely defined, which is part of the reason why the most powerful applications of computers to management lie in the future. But preliminary studies indicate that a statement made originally in connection with military matters also holds for the business world: "Men in command once believed that it was impossible for a computer to assist them in dealing with problems which they had spent lifetimes studying—and still did not understand. That position is no longer tenable." The same thing might be said for problems involving legislatures, Federal agencies, and other large organizations.

In any case, within its brief lifetime the computer has become indispensable in many areas. The evidence is ample, and it is no longer a matter of occasional projects undertaken on an experimental basis. There are laboratories where the machines function regularly as a tool for research, and the M.I.T. Computation Center is one of the most successful. Sponsored by the International Business Machines Corporation, the world's leading manufacturer of calculating machines, it is headed by Philip Morse and serves investigators at more than thirty New England colleges and universities.

The Center opened in June, 1957, and a recent report summarizes results of its first three years. During that period about a thousand different problems were studied involving practically all the areas we have mentioned so far, as well as a good many we have not mentioned. The following titles indicate the scope of the projects: Fallout Radioactivity in Rainwater, A Dynamic Model of Competition between Two Firms, A Heuristic Strategy for Computer Game Playing, United Nations Office Operation, Shop Motions in Irregular Waves.

The thing to remember is that all the problems were run on a single computer, a model known as the IBM 704. But it could have been any one of a number of other commercial machines such as the IBM 709 or 7090 or a Remington Rand Univac (Universal Automatic Computer), or Control Data Corporation's 1604. It could have been the machine in Princeton which was designed by the late John von Neumann, the great Hungarian-born mathematician, and his associates at the Institute for Advanced Study. It could also have been one of the machines built along similar lines and bearing a variety of intriguing names—JOHNNIAC (named after von Neumann) at the Rand Corporation in California, MANIAC at Los Alamos, ILLIAC at the University of Illinois, ORACLE at Oak Ridge, or MYSTIC at Michigan State University.

The main point is that the general-purpose computer represents a new breed of machine, and a most peculiar breed at that. It is sure to evolve rapidly, but chances are that, in the near future at least, its basic structure will not change radically. It will be made up of units performing the same basic functions. A system of wires and transistors and switches and panels, it occupies its allotted space, apparently another piece of electronic hardware. Yet in a sense—and this has never been quite as valid before—this machine is far more than it appears to be. It is a unique challenge. After every problem it solves, it confronts you with a persistent and disturbing question: "What next?"

Take the most subtle problem yet put to a computer. The investigator knows that if he could devise an even more subtle problem right away, on the spot, the machine could solve it. More than that, he knows that during the years ahead the machine will be able to solve a large number of still more subtle problems which he and his colleagues will be thinking up—but cannot yet specify. One of the things he does *not* know, however, is the machine's limits. From this standpoint, the machine is always ahead of him and will be ahead of him for an indefinite future.

The computer is probably the first and only machine ever made by man whose full capabilities, as things stand now, remain unknown to its makers. So we are not merely exploring natural phenomena in computer laboratories. We are also exploring the machines themselves and, at a deeper level, the power of the human brain. It is no wonder that research on computers is attracting more and more attention, particularly the attention of young investigators. The rush is on. Computers are being bombarded with every imaginable type of practical and theoretical question and, like child prodigies, manage to answer the questions as fast as they come up.

But the pressure is heavy. In his Computation Center report, Professor Morse writes of the available equipment: "Its use has doubled in the past three years; it probably would have tripled if the computer capacity had not been saturated this last year; it will probably increase by another factor of 2 or 3 in the next three years if the machine capacity can be kept abreast of the demand. The staff of the Center must continue its efforts to increase the flexibility and efficiency of the equipment."

Meanwhile veteran companies have been stepping up

the manufacture of general-purpose electronic computers, and new companies are entering the picture. Here are some estimates of production rates within the next few years (considering the way the demand has been skyrocketing, it would be a risky business to prophesy for a much longer future). By 1965 the number of large commercial computers operating in the United States will have jumped from 700 to more than 3,000. In general the policy is to rent rather than sell the machines, and they will bring an annual rental of about $1,125,000,000.

The pace of events is so swift that even technical journals cannot keep up with it. This book should not be regarded as an attempt to cover the entire field. It presents the history of the electronic computer, elementary principles of how it operates and is designed, and some examples of current applications as well as applications being planned for the near future. It also presents some ideas involving the powers of computers as compared with the powers of the human brain. This part of the book first discusses recent notions about the structure and workings of the brain, indicating how it resembles and differs from existing computers. Then we shall describe certain research projects which will influence the use and design of later generations of computers—and which are influencing our notions of how the brain operates.

I hope it will become clear that writing a book about computers is almost the same thing as writing a book about research itself. The study of these machines is intimately related to the study of how we acquire scientific knowledge. The evolution of computers is a significant part of human evolution, and an appreciation of their importance may provide fresh insights into our place as the most rapidly evolving species on earth.

CHAPTER 2

COUNTERS—FROM FINGERS TO TRANSISTORS

> At a period when the progress of physical science is obstructed by that exhausting intellectual and mental labor indispensable for its advancement . . . I think the application of machinery in aid of the most complicated and abstruse calculations can no longer be deemed unworthy of the attention of the country. In fact there is no reason why mental as well as bodily labor should not be economized by the aid of machinery.

Charles Babbage, the English mathematician and inventor who wrote these words more than a hundred years ago, is the first great pioneer in the history of the automatic computer. He not only recognized the need for such a machine at a time when few people did, but saw quite clearly how it would have to operate. Furthermore, he spent a major portion of his time and personal fortune figuring out a way to build it. He even had a name for it, the "analytical engine."

The inventor never had a chance to construct his engine. People were interested. Philosophically minded scientists and laymen speculated then as now about the powers of machines that could do some of the things that brains do. The British government was interested, too, but not sufficiently to come up with funds. It had already given Babbage about $80,000 for another less ambitious mathematical machine which had not been completed, and decided that the analytical engine was impractical. Perhaps the government had a bit of a point there. Industry still had a great deal to learn about the precision machining of mechanical parts. Compact and highly efficient relay switches—developed largely for the telephone industry—did not exist, and, of course, more than half a century was to pass before the coming of reliable vacuum tubes.

If Babbage had ever succeeded in building his computer, it would have ranked as one of the mechanical marvels of all time. It would have been a miniature universe of wheels within wheels, a supermechanism of 50,000 wheels or gears —plus quantities of clutches, tangs, escapements, cams, axles, and cranks. Compared to it the most complicated piece of clockwork yet devised would seem like a child's Tinker Toy creation. We know this because when the inventor died in 1871, he left a small library of plans. There were 400 to 500 pages of special schematic symbols to represent mechanical parts and connections, five volumes of engineering sketches, and more than 400 detailed drawings.

Some of this material is so abstruse that it still baffles curious investigators. But it shows beyond doubt that Babbage was on the right track, and that he combined an ability to think in concrete "hardware" terms with an unusually active imagination. Unfortunately, his contemporary Jules Verne neglected to use the analytical engine as the theme for a science-fiction tale. It would have made instructive reading, for the machine embodied certain fundamental principles which are just as valid now as they were in Victorian times.

The engine was to include two parts, a "store" and a "mill." The store represented an ingenious mechanical memory and contained the numbers to be used in solving particular equations. The mill, as the name implies, was intended to do the mathematical work. According to design plans, it could receive numbers from the store, perform arithmetic operations on them, and put intermediate numbers back into the store for future reference. Store and mill were to be linked by a series of wheels whose motions were adjusted to transmit numerical information. As we shall see, modern computers incorporate circuits which are the electronic descendants of such mechanical devices.

Babbage also worked out a remarkably farsighted way of feeding information into the machine and furnishing a predetermined sequence of orders to be followed automatically. He did this by using something which is still a familiar item in the fearsome world of twentieth-century paper work, the punch card. We have ample firsthand experience with these omnipresent items in our impersonal dealings with telephone companies, income-tax bureaus, magazine subscription departments, and so on. They evolved from an ancestor which appeared during the early violent days of the Industrial Revolution.

In 1801 a Frenchman named Joseph Jacquard built a loom which wove brocaded silks and used cards with patterns of holes in them. Different patterns permitted different thread-grasping wire hooks to fall through the holes, thus controlling certain operations required to reproduce artists' designs. This step had formerly been done by hand, and within a decade 11,000 of the machines were at work in French textile plants. But there was plenty of trouble at first. There was technological unemployment, a problem which still confronts us today in the development of computer-controlled automatic factories. Displaced workers took the law into their own hands and smashed a number of the new looms, cards and all. (Jacquard wrote: "The iron was sold for iron, the wood for wood, and I its inventor was delivered up to public ignominy.")

Babbage decided to use similar cards in communicating with the analytical engine. His cards were linked together to form a chain and also allowed selected wires to drop through strategically placed holes. There were two decks of cards. One deck selected the numbers which were to be extracted from the store. The other determined what operations the mill would perform on the numbers. Design plans also called for special punch cards to be used when the machine needed certain information it did not have. At such a stage it would ring a bell, summoning an attendant who would produce the required number in punch-card form and insert it into a convenient slot. Checking devices would examine the number. If it was correct, calculations would proceed in due course. If not, the machine would "ring a louder bell and stop."

Babbage worked for some twenty years on the machine, and although it remained in the blueprint stage, he felt that his plans were fundamentally sound. He had this to say in his autobiography, *The Life of a Philosopher*: "If, unwarned by my example, any man shall undertake and shall succeed in really constructing an engine embodying in itself the whole of the executive department of mathematical analysis upon different principles or by simpler mechanical means—I have no fear of leaving my reputation in his charge, for he alone will be fully able to appreciate the nature of my efforts and the value of their results."

Whether or not Babbage's engine was too complicated to build in the nineteenth century, the fact remains that a long time passed before his ideas were translated into a full-time working model. Not until World War II did the first large-scale digital, or counting, computer go into regular operation. Completed by IBM and Harvard scientists in 1944, it was an electromechanical system using telephone-type relay switches as counters—and, of course, punch cards. The first of the giant electronic machines which dominate the field today, and which are the main subject of this book, came about a year later. Its designers were John W. Mauchly and J. P. Eckert, Jr., of the Moore School of Electrical Engineering at the University of Pennsylvania. Known as ENIAC, Electronic Numerical Integrator and Computer, it was definitely a war baby.

A shortage of human computers helped bring ENIAC into existence. Military scientists and engineers were producing new shooting weapons, and various models of each weapon for troops in the field—new howitzers, antiaircraft guns, antitank guns, in all shapes and sizes. Every one of these guns required ballistic tables indicating trajectories for different elevations, types of shell, wind directions, and other important variables. To compute a single trajectory for a given set of conditions required about seven hours' work at a desk computer. Hundreds of adding-machine operators worked day and night pushing buttons and cranking out calculations, and if there is any duller work, I cannot imagine it. It was assembly-line monotony with a vengeance. Furthermore, human computers could not keep up with the pace of warfare, and weapons often went to the battlefield without ballistic tables.

The construction of ENIAC started as part of a drive to break this information bottleneck. In fact, a memo dated August, 1942, and outlining the project had been gathering dust for nearly a year when it was unearthed by a mathematician in uniform, Lt. Herman Goldstine of the Army's Ballistics Research Laboratory in Aberdeen, Maryland (and now one of IBM's top-ranking investigators). He was in Philadelphia trying to recruit more girls to operate adding machines, happened to visit friends at the

Moore School, saw the memo, and hastened to set things moving in Washington. The project was approved within two weeks. Although ENIAC never became involved in actual war work (it was completed about two months after Japan surrendered), it represented a major advance in automatic computing.

To be sure, the machine was not all it might have been. Built under the pressure of wartime schedules, it was hardly an example of engineering finesse. For one thing, it was rather bulky. It occupied 1,500 square feet of floor space and weighed more than 30 tons. It included miles of wires, half a million soldered connections, and about twenty thousand vacuum tubes. A television set with only twelve to fifteen tubes may become fairly hot, so you can imagine how much heat ENIAC generated. It was a potential furnace as well as a computer. An air-conditioning system helped keep the operating level down to about 100 degrees Fahrenheit, and the machine was designed to shut itself off automatically when the air conditioning failed. Otherwise, temperatures would have soared, and it would have melted its own connections.

A more serious difficulty was that ENIAC had a notable tendency to break down without warning. An investigator who spent long hours caring for the machine in the early days had this to say about his experiences: "We had plenty of trouble, mostly of an engineering nature and often associated with poor solder connections. This sort of error curls your teeth. Every once in a while a unit failed to respond. For example, it refused to register a number. Or numbers that should be positive suddenly became negative, or answers came out that were ridiculously large. You look for the flaw, but everything seems to be working perfectly. So you give up. Then as soon as you try running your problem again, the machine acts up and you have to start all over again."

Early one evening, for example, ENIAC went mysteriously berserk. Five hundred tubes in one of the arithmetic units, plus 3,500 associated tubes, kept flashing off and on. But no answer came out. To complicate matters, every once in a while the machine settled down and began operating normally—only to go berserk again. Investigators finally located the trouble at 5 A.M. the next day. It was roughly the equivalent of dropping a monkey wrench in the gears. A bit of wire about $\frac{1}{16}$ inch long had fallen across contacts in a terminal box and was producing a short circuit, so that the machine repeated itself over and over. From time to time vibrations of the air-conditioning fans apparently jiggled the wire enough to break the short circuit, and then to make it again. All things considered, compared with today's more highly evolved machines, ENIAC was a somewhat temperamental electronic dinosaur.

Despite these and other troubles, however, ENIAC soon demonstrated its mathematical powers. Investigators lost no time putting the machine to a severe test. Problem No. 1, a top-secret job for the Los Alamos Scientific Laboratory in New Mexico, demanded solutions to some stubborn equations describing the build-up of energy in atomic weapons. The problem called for a massive number of arithmetic operations, about enough to take 100 man-years on adding machines, and had already proved far too difficult for any existing computer. ENIAC solved it in two months, including a month during which mathematicians were learning to prepare the problem in a form suitable for the machine. Problem No. 2, which involved the checking of a theory about nuclear fission, required less than two weeks.

ENIAC was the trailblazer. While it was being built, people who saw problems far more clearly than possibilities—and the world is full of them—had argued that the machine would never work. They had a valid point; they always do. According to manufacturers' guarantees, vacuum tubes would last for 2,500 hours. Given this figure, there is no getting around the conclusion that in a machine with some 20,000 tubes, a tube would fail every eighth of an hour on the average—that is, every 7½ minutes. The argument seemed to be unanswerable, and if designers had taken it at its face value, we would have no computers today.

What actually happened was that Mauchly and Eckert and their associates recognized the problem and sought for ways out of the apparent impasse. They sampled tube lots, soon found that most of the tubes were considerably longer lived than the guarantees specified (2,500 hours was a minimum figure), and simply discarded less hardy tubes in advance. Furthermore, they raised longevity still further by underloading the tubes, using only half the power for which the elements had been designed. What it all added up to in practical day-to-day operation was that a tube failed only every two days or so, rather than every 7½ minutes.

This accomplishment and others convinced some of the skeptics. The enthusiasts needed no convincing. They were ready to attack in time of peace problems which had to be shelved during the war. Even before ENIAC was completed, they were considering plans for new and improved machines with fewer tubes and higher speeds and greater flexibility. Interest quickened when John von Neumann decided to build a machine for basic research at the Institute for Advanced Study, and investigators elsewhere stepped up their studies. The results of their efforts are the large-scale electronic machines which have become standbys in many laboratories and other organizations throughout the world, and which represent the forerunners of still more advanced machines.

In the modern computer we have invented a device of

almost limitless possibilities. We have yet to understand its nature completely, or to learn what it can and cannot do. It may be regarded, among other things, as a unique kind of communications system. It has built-in logic and built-in rules and an internal organization too subtle for any one scientist or engineer to know in full detail. It runs silent with no visible moving parts. But it is a center of seething electronic activity and runs at inconceivable speeds. On its private time scale, in this constructed world of signals, events proceed so swiftly that a few hours for the machine are a lifetime for a man. Nothing in familiar experience involves such an enormous acceleration of time.

Suppose that you are located on some ideal viewing platform and can observe at a panoramic glance the entire traffic flow of a large city. Cars stream continuously in and out of the city, at different speeds and with different destinations. Entering on main traffic arteries, they move in complex paths, dipping and rising along straight stretches and sweeping curves and cloverleaf loops. They pass over and under each other in places where elevated highways crisscross in multilevel patterns.

At red lights they halt in long lines like soldiers standing at attention, while other cars pass before them on intersecting routes. The lights change and waiting cars start up again. Still heading for their destinations, they move off the superhighways into intricate networks of avenues, boulevards, two-way streets, one-way streets, little side streets, dead-end streets. All cars come at last to specific places, addresses where they are parked and wait for a time. Then the whole cycle repeats itself. They start moving again. They pull out of parking locations, back through and out of the networks, against the stream of other cars still coming in.

Now imagine a motion picture in which events are speeded up many thousands of times. Years of traffic flow take only a few minutes on the screen, daily cycles become flashes of activity, split-second traffic pulses. If such a film existed and you could see the results, you would have an idea of some of the things that go on in a computer. We can think of a computer as a sort of metropolis, a region of many zones and addresses confined within definite boundaries. It includes networks in which directed traffic moves along carefully laid out routes—a traffic of information or signals, electrical pulses, bursts of electrons. The signals start, stop, arrive at destinations, and start again in precisely timed sequences.

There are different kinds of large-scale electronic computers, but in all cases the major sections or blocks are the same. Here is a highly simplified block diagram, one way of showing the general layout of a computer:

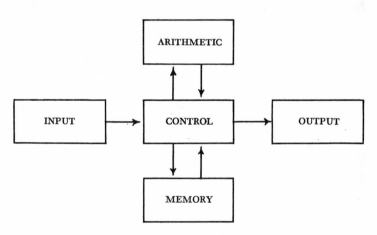

The input unit enables us to communicate with the machine, to provide it with numbers and instructions for handling the numbers. In setting up a problem this information enters in coded form—say, as the holes in punch cards or punch tape—and ends up in the memory unit, where it is stored ready for use.

Then a button is pushed, problem-solving starts, and the control unit takes over. It extracts instructions and numbers from the memory unit and passes the numbers on to the arithmetic unit where adding, subtracting, and so on take place. There is constant two-way traffic between control, memory, and arithmetic units. When the required answers have been obtained, the machine's job is done and it communicates the new information to investigators by means of the output unit, for example, an electric typewriter.

Notice that the entire system shown in the block diagram is roughly analogous to a man operating an adding machine or desk calculator. In this case the input is the problem he is told to solve, perhaps a series of a hundred numbers and the instruction to add them. If he receives the numbers and instruction in written form, the piece of paper may be regarded as the memory unit, a way of storing information. The calculator, of course, is the arithmetic unit and does all the mathematical work; the final sum is the output.

The man himself represents the control unit. It is his job to select number after number, press the appropriate keys for each number, and pull the crank periodically until all the numbers have been added together. A problem as simple as this one is hardly worth bringing to the attention of a giant electronic computer, which could dash off the entire summing process in about a hundredth of a second. But similar principles apply to the automatic solution of enormously more difficult problems.

The block diagram tells us nothing about what happens inside the units. Each unit contains many electronic parts, but there is nothing mysterious about it. We can speak of machines obeying orders, remembering, and even thinking as long as we bear in mind that these and other functions are performed using basic circuits which may be less complicated than the circuits in our television sets. The trick lies in combining relatively simple circuits into an organized system. Since the computers to be discussed are essentially high-speed automatic counting devices, we shall first describe the counters themselves, the arithmetic units.

Counting always involves motion. Whenever there is counting to be done, you have to move something from one place to another, from one position to another. Take the original, prehistoric counter—the finger. This handy device is not as simple as it seems. In fact, it even involves a kind of biological electronics. The decision to move a finger into counting position originates somewhere in the brain, and passes downstream along nerve fibers as electrical pulses. At the end of the line are special fibers wrapped neatly around muscle cells. When the pulses reach these fibers, certain muscles contract and your finger moves. But the process takes time. About a quarter of a second passes between the decision and the action, a single count.

Now we can go one step further, to a more advanced counter. The counters in a desk calculator are gears, and again it takes energy and time to move them. Each gear has ten teeth, tiny levers pushed by other intermeshed gear teeth and representing the digits o through 9. In adding-machine operations a gear makes a count, moves one position, in about a tenth of a second. Another type of counter includes various switches resembling those used to flick lights off and on, or to make a connection between outside power lines and home terminal boxes. The highly efficient switches which go into operation and count when you dial a telephone number, move from one position to another in a hundredth of a second or so.

A vacuum tube can also be used as a counting switch, although its moving elements are not so obvious. The things that move inside a tube are negatively charged subatomic particles, electrons. They have little mass and their inertia, their resistance to stopping and starting, is extremely low. An "off" vacuum tube is something like a break in a circuit. When the tube is "turned on," or fired, the circuit is closed in a switching action. Charged particles move across a gap between electrodes, and this process represents an electronic count. It may take place within a ten millionth of a second or less. (Transistors, the tiny metallic, or semiconductor, crystals which are replacing tubes in radio and television sets and many other devices, work in an analogous fashion.)

As far as sheer speed is concerned, technology has brought far more spectacular advances in counting than in transportation. A rocket may travel five or ten thousand times faster than a man on foot, but counting speeds from fingers to vacuum tubes or transistors have increased millions of times—and that difference is an important factor in the effectiveness of electronic computers. ENIAC, for example, worked on a simple and straightforward principle. It did its calculating with the aid of so-called "decade counters."

For simplicity's sake, such a device may be considered as a circuit containing ten vacuum tubes arranged in a ring like the figures on the face of a wristwatch. Each tube may be conducting electricity or not, on or off. The ten tubes are interconnected in such a way that if they are all in the off position and a single pulse enters the circuit, the No. 1 tube is switched on. Another pulse switches the No. 1 tube off and the No. 2 tube on; still another pulse douses the No. 2 tube and turns tube No. 3 on; and so on around the ring.

ENIAC's arithmetic unit was designed to handle numbers up to ten digits long. So you can think of ten such rings lined up one next to the other, like a row of ten clocks or the ten parallel gears in a ten-digit desk calculator. As a matter of fact, the vacuum-tube rings do exactly what counting gears do, each tube being the equivalent of a gear tooth—and a decade counter is, in effect, an electronic gear. (Actually instead of a single tube at each digit position, the counter has a pair of tubes hooked up together so that one is always off when the other is on. Such a pair is known as a "flip-flop.")

Such devices plus their associated circuits represent an early application of vacuum tubes as calculating elements. But modern machines differ as widely from the veteran ENIAC as jet planes differ from the Wright brothers' Kitty Hawk model, and one of the most significant differences is that the newcomers have another way of doing arithmetic. The story of this development takes us back to a consideration of finger counting. The number system we use, the decimal system, is largely the result of a biological circumstance—namely, the fact that during the long course of evolution we happen to have appeared as ten-fingered animals, natural-born decade devices. Because we have ten fingers on our hands, we also have ten digits and count by tens. It is understandable that, as far as this single characteristic goes, we built ENIAC in our own image.

But many number systems have been invented besides ours, and one of them, known as the binary system, is more appropriate for electronic computers. Decimal numbers are shorthand for sums of "subnumbers"—ones, tens, hundreds, thousands, and so on. Thus, if we were just learning the system, 230 could be written in the following tabular form:

Hundreds	Tens	Ones
2	3	0

In other words, this number is the sum of 2 hundreds, 3

tens, and o ones. The digits o through 9 serve to indicate how many subnumbers there are in each column or place. Of course, we are so accustomed to our way of reckoning that we do not need tables to help us arrange decimal digits in proper combinations.

The binary system is something else again. It uses only two digits, o and 1, instead of ten. A binary number, like the decimal variety, represents a series of additions. But since it is made up of only two kinds of digits, it can do no more than indicate the presence or absence of its component subnumbers. It is always a string of o's and 1's. For example, here is how decimal 13 would be expressed in binary terms:

Eight	Four	Two	One
1	1	o	1

So decimal 13 is binary 1101—or 1 eight, 1 four, o two, and 1 one. We need a bigger table to express decimal 230 as a binary number:

One hundred twenty-eight	Sixty-four	Thirty-two	Sixteen	Eight	Four	Two	One
1	1	1	o	o	1	1	o

The binary number 11100110 simply tells you to add 128, 64, 32, 4, and 2.

At first this method of writing numbers seems strange. But with a bit of practice you can get used to it. The main question is why we should use it in computers. Part of the answer is that you need fewer vacuum tubes. To register a ten-place number, ENIAC required one decade counter of ten flip-flops (twenty tubes) for each place, or 200 tubes in all. Now the binary system requires more places for a given number than the decimal system, roughly three times as many on the average. But even so, it is more economical. A ten-place decimal number written in binary terms takes about thirty-three places, which means thirty-three flip-flops or sixty-six tubes—and that is appreciably less than 200 tubes.

That difference signifies a deeper and more fundamental difference. To make an electronic computer count in the decimal system amounts to imposing on it methods which are right for us but not for it. A vacuum tube has two, not ten, natural states which you can express in various ways: lit or unlit, on or off, 1 or 0, signal or no signal. A tube is a sort of one-fingered device—and computers based on the binary system are faster and more efficient as well as more economical of tubes. In a fundamental sense, binary digits, or "bits," represent the simplest way of expressing information. Notice that 0 conveys as much information as 1, that the absence of a signal can be as meaningful as a signal.

For a general idea of the binary system in action consider a very simple four-bit computer. This hypothetical machine adds binary numbers up to a total of 1111 (decimal 15), and has an arithmetic unit for the purpose. Included in the unit is a register which holds numbers drawn out of the machine's memory and an "accumulator" where the totals actually appear. The register consists of four vacuum tubes in a row, the second and fourth being on, the first and third being off. That is, the register holds binary number 0101 (decimal 5).

The accumulator also has a row of four vacuum tubes; only the third tube is on, representing binary 0010 (decimal 2). Each tube in the accumulator is wired to a corresponding tube in the register. A special type of circuit is hooked into each connection between a register tube and an accumulator tube. This is called an "AND circuit" and is so designed that no electricity can pass through if it is receiving signals from a single source: it must receive a signal from each of two different sources at the same time. The following diagram shows the present condition of the arithmetic unit:

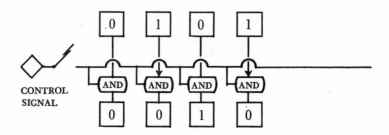

The diamond at the extreme left is a control-signal source with a telegraph-key switch whose function will be explained shortly. The tubes are indicated by squares containing binary digits or bits, 0101 in the register (top row) and 0010 in the accumulator. On the upper, or register, level the second and fourth tubes are on, which means they each feed a signal into their corresponding AND circuits. But since these circuits require two signals, no electricity is passing to the lower accumulator tubes.

Now imagine that you press down on the telegraph key, which closes the switch. Electricity immediately flows to the entire system. It flows to the first AND circuit, where nothing happens, since the circuit is receiving only one signal. But the second AND circuit receives signals from two sources, from its register tube and from the control-signal source, and allows current to flow downstream. So the lower accumulator tube conducts electricity, going from 0 to 1. The same thing happens in the fourth register-AND-accumulator column. The third column behaves like the first. Its register tube was off to start with, so that even when the AND circuit receives a signal, that is the only signal. So there is no change in the lower accumulator tube; it is already on. This diagram shows the new state of affairs in the arithmetic unit:

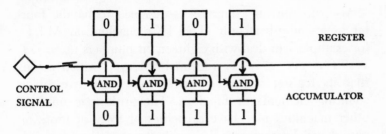

The net effect of closing the switch is to produce a 111 in the accumulator, which is exactly what we want—since 0101 (decimal 5) plus 0010 (decimal 2) equals 0111 (decimal 7). Then the switch automatically flips up, cutting off the control-signal source.

So much for the first step. Pressing another key clears the register to 0000. Pressing again will bring a new number flashing into the register from the memory unit. Press still another key, and the new number is added to the number already in the accumulator. And so on. The elementary computer responds as fast as the switches are opened and closed, performing an operation with every electrical pulse coming from the control-signal source. Every pulse acts as a trigger in this machine-gun kind of system which works in periodical bursts of activity and, within its narrow limits, produces accurate answers.

A real-life computer has considerably more impressive capacities. Its arithmetic unit involves a rich variety of additional circuits to handle many other operations. To cite one case in point, notice that our four-bit device lacks the hardware necessary to "carry" from one place to another. The statement 7 plus 2 equals 9 becomes 0111 plus 0010 equals 1001 in binary lingo, and we have included no circuits to perform the carrying operation over to the extra place. Working computers have such circuits and also circuits for multiplication, division, and subtraction as well as addition.

Also, no existing computer is designed to handle four-bit binary numbers only. The TX-0 machine at M.I.T., for example, can deal with eighteen-bit numbers up to 111, 111, 111, 111, 111, 111 (decimal 262,144)—which means that its register and accumulator rows include eighteen counting elements or flip-flops. The arithmetic units of other machines may have capacities of forty or more binary digits. Furthermore TX-0, like most of the new computers, contains thousands of transistors which replace tubes, produce little heat, last at least twice as long as tubes, require less power, and take up less space.

Finally of course, there is no pressing of keys. The pulses which trigger operations are under automatic control, and for some of the most effective circuitry used in such applications computer engineers owe a great deal to their colleagues in television. The action you see on your television screen is the result of a sort of movie process, thirty pictures being produced every second. Each picture is a mosaic made up of about 240,000 dots of light of different intensities, and special circuits scan the entire array thirty times a second. In other words, every second the circuits produce 240,000 times 30, or 7,200,000 scanning pulses. If you are interested, you can figure out how many pulses your eyes are exposed to during a one-hour show.

Similar pulse-producing circuits control counting in computers. Timing is vital in this control system. The TX-0 machine has precisely synchronized cycles each taking two-millionths of a second and including eight individual pulses. Each pulse triggers an operation and represents a working period. Pulsing circuits are superpacemakers. The computing speed of any machine is related to the rate or frequency of its pulses, to the barrages of rhythmical electronic beats which drive it.

Present-day speeds are spectacular, particularly when compared with our limited abilities in this respect. How long would it take you to multiply two ten-place numbers? I was told it would take four or five minutes, and decided to try it. The estimate was fairly close, except for one thing. I spent about five minutes doing the multiplication the first time, and another five minutes or so checking the answer, which turned out to be wrong. So any comparison between calculating with paper and pencil and calculating with the aid of a machine should take into account the fact that the machine is generally more reliable for time-consuming problems. A desk calculator, by the way, could multiply two ten-place numbers in about ten seconds flat.

To illustrate the abilities of the electronic computer we can take a specific example, the problem I worked on with paper and pencil—3,696,437,692 times 9,731,991,327. Suppose we were to use IBM's STRETCH, a speed champion housed at the Los Alamos Scientific Laboratory. The machine is capable of multiplying these two numbers and coming up with the correct answer (35,973,699,559,339,-897,284) in one-half of a millionth of a second. To put it another way, it can multiply 500,000 pairs of ten-digit numbers a second. As far as the kind of thinking required for arithmetic is concerned, electronic computers clearly operate many times faster than we do. We shall see later that this is one of their most significant powers.

This brings us roughly up to date on computer speeds, "roughly" because the way things have been moving during the past years, records may be broken almost as quickly as they are set. The arithmetic units of early electronic machines drew heavily on experience acquired in many fields. One of the first steps in building ENIAC was to obtain circuits designed to serve a variety of purposes—counters for recording cosmic rays and radioactive decay, special clocking devices, instruments used in making high-speed X rays, radar pulsing units. We have already pointed out that the counters in contemporary computers are based on television circuits and other developments in industries which were just starting or nonexistent during World War II.

No one can tell for certain where tomorrow's counters will come from. They may arise out of research in low-temperature physics, magnetism, crystal structure, or even out of work on giant biological molecules. As investigators with different scientific backgrounds enter the computer field, it is increasingly difficult to predict future break-throughs. The same situation exists in other areas. In certain respects various branches of science are becoming more and more closely related—and the computer is one striking result of this notable trend.

CHAPTER 3

COMMUNICATING WITH COMPUTERS

CONTRARY TO POPULAR IMPRESSIONS, there is a great deal more to computers than high-speed counting devices. A story about a machine that ran wild illustrates this point. The story may or may not be apocryphal. Some investigators take it quite literally, and those who believe everything they see in print will inform you that it appears in a book about computers. Other investigators are convinced that the tale has been embellished in successive retellings. In any case, science like any other area of culture has a right to its legends, if it is a legend.

The minor catastrophe was ultimately traced to an oversight. It occurred during the early days when the machines and their users were less accustomed to working with one another than they are now. One day, according to a recent version of the incident, a computer suffered "the electronic equivalent of a nervous breakdown." Left unattended for the night, it began a long series of calculations on what was intended to be a routine and rational problem. Its circuits delivered appropriate pulses and its counters operated at a rapid rate, but for some reason the solution never came. The machine never turned itself off. By the time investigators returned to the scene, they found the computer in a state of shock. Although still operating in a crazy sort of way, it was not getting anywhere and had blown out a number of its tubes.

The story goes on to explain the source of the trouble. The machine had been wrestling with a problem too big for its capacities, and also too big for the capacities of any human computer. Divide a number, say 1,000, by successively smaller fractions—1/2, 1/50, 1/1,000 and so on —and the answers will be larger and larger numbers. In other words, the smaller the fraction you divide by, the greater the final quotient. It follows that if you divide by zero, the quotient becomes infinitely large. To shield children from the hazards of dealing prematurely with infinity, we teach them that in doing arithmetic they are not to try dividing by zero. Unfortunately, mathematicians forgot to relay similar instructions to the machine.

One of the morals to be drawn from this story is that chaos may result when we do not provide a computer with complete information. If we tell it to undertake an impossible task, it will obey us to the letter. And unless we provide it with some criteria for recognizing impossibility, it will work at a solution until it is shut off. A computer may have the fastest counting devices available, the best arithmetic unit, but at present it is not much better than the orders it receives. Modern machines do not blow out tubes in efforts to solve the unsolvable, although, as we shall see, preparing orders continues to be a major area of research.

Assume for the time being that the investigator has already written out a suitable step-by-step program of what he wants the machine to do. The next problem is to translate the program. The machine's natural language is a binary language. It reads, writes, and "speaks" only in terms of the binary digits 0 and 1. Everything we tell it must be translated into these digits, and that goes for the entire computer system—the input, memory, control, and output units as well as the arithmetic unit.

There are a number of ways of changing our symbols into terms that the machine can understand. In one method the first step involves a special typewriter. Instead of printing letters and characters, the typewriter operates an automatic device which punches holes in a paper tape about an inch wide. If the typist sees the number 53 on the program, he simply strikes the right keys and a row of precisely placed holes appears on the tape.

The punched holes represent binary 1's, and the absent holes, or unpunched places, binary 0's. Thus the typist punches a sequence representing 110101, the binary number for 53.

We may translate words as well as numbers. This has been done for years in telegraph offices and news bureaus where teletype devices, also using punched tape and the binary system, receive and send messages. Sets of five 0's and 1's, no-holes and holes in various combinations, represent individual letters on the teletype tapes and on computer tapes. Thus, 10001 11000 11000 might stand for "add," and other combinations for other words used in computer programs. (Notice that 10001 11000 11000 could stand for the decimal numbers 17, 24, and 24 as well as for "add." The machine is not confused, however, for designers have devised methods of distinguishing operational instructions. For example, the first part of an order could always be instruction words, and the second part numbers.)

Such an approach may seem like a long-winded way of spelling things out. But this is not a serious problem because information can be fed into machines rapidly. The tape-sensing element or input unit of a computer is an efficient and relatively simple device. The tape unreels between a light source and a system of photoelectric cells or "electric eyes," like those used to operate burglar alarms or doors which open as you approach. Now imagine that a row of holes and no-holes, 110101, moves under the light. In the third and fifth positions, where there are no holes, no light passes through the tape and the photoelectric cells at these positions do not respond since they receive no signals. But rays pass through each of the other four positions, triggering four corresponding cells. The cells send patterns of electrical pulses into the machine, coded messages which make up the only language the machine understands.

The idea of punched tape is not new. The same general principle is found in the perforated paper rolls which fitted into old player pianos, different patterns of holes serving as codes for different tunes. In fact, you can go back further than that to the first half of the nineteenth century. Bands of perforated paper were used before punch cards to control weaving designs on textile looms. Of course, as we indicated in the preceding chapter, punch cards themselves are employed in many present-day computers. Input units built for them have brushes which sweep across the surfaces of cards and make electrical contacts wherever there are holes.

Another way of coding information for computers involves the special kind of tape developed for recording sound and televised material. This tape has no holes. It contains "spots" magnetized in opposite directions, one direction representing 0 and the other 1. The spots are sensed by input units with electromagnetic devices that register the spots and translate them into the usual electrical pulses. Magnetic tape is often used instead of the paper variety for long programs of computer instructions, programs requiring more than a hundred feet or so of tape. Among other things, it is more compact; that is, you can pack more information into the same space.

Modern input devices can convey a great deal in a relatively brief period. Paper tape unreels fast enough so that in a minute the machine may read more than 800,000 binary digits, or bits. Since bits are units of information, we can express that figure in different terms. An average book may contain some four hundred words to a page, which comes to a total of about ten thousand bits. So punched-tape equipment delivers eighty pages of information to this computer every minute. At that rate, it would take roughly a day to put into the machine the entire quantity of information contained in the twenty-four volumes of the *Encyclopaedia Britannica*—that is, if there were only some place to put all the facts.

Ever since ENIAC there has been a steady demand for increased storage space. We are caught in an upward-spiraling process, and the end is not in sight. As soon as designers manage to develop a new and more voluminous type of computer memory, investigators promptly come up with new problems which call for still larger memories. If we compare a computer to a city in miniature whose traffic consists of coded pulses, then the computer's memory unit may be thought of as a great parking lot—a center where individual bits of information enter, occupy their places for a time, move out, and enter again. In computers as in cities it is quite a job to handle the flow of traffic in and out of such parking locations.

The memory units in most common use today are made up of magnetic devices, so-called "magnetic cores." Jay W. Forrester of M.I.T. first developed them about ten years ago when he was working on Whirlwind, the fastest computer of its day. At the time, one of his tasks involved designing a prototype machine for the Air Force, and he had good reasons for deciding to try something besides vacuum tubes as storage elements. Whirlwind had a nasty habit of breaking down frequently, usually because of failures among the tubes of the memory unit. Magnetic cores helped reduce the failure rate hundreds of times and now play a major role in the computers used in SAGE, the nation's air-defense system, as well as in most other machines.

A magnetic core is simply a washer- or doughnut-shaped element which can be magnetized in one of two directions as follows:

By this time we have had enough of the binary system to know what the directions of magnetization mean. The clockwise direction can represent a o, the counterclockwise direction a 1. A memory unit consists of an array of such cores wired together in an intricate network so that they are connected with one another and indirectly with the sensing elements of the input unit. The pulses produced by the photoelectric cells which read paper tape, for example, flash to the memory unit and leave records of themselves on impressionable magnetic cores. Here are diagrams of a sixteen-bit memory before and after receiving numerical information:

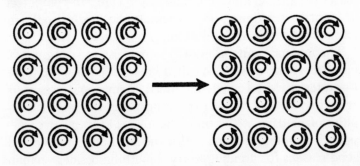

The cores at the left are all magnetized in the clockwise direction, which means they are all set at binary o. At the right is the same array after it has taken on its load of information, the cores magnetized in the counterclockwise direction being 1's. The array holds four lines of magnetically represented bits: 1110, 1001, 1101, and 1011 (decimal 14, 9, 13, and 11, respectively). A typical computer array may be made up of 4,096 cores (a 64 by 64 square) on a flat wire grid which, in the words of one designer, "resembles a repair patch on a copper screen." Such arrays are stacked one above the other like the floors of a building.

Magnetic-core memories are extremely compact. Each core is only about fifty-thousandths of an inch in diameter, or about as big around as a BB shot. A vacuum-tube memory may take up the space of a junior executive's office, aside from the problem of the heat it generates. The cool core memory of the TX-o computer, which contains thirty-eight 4,096-bit arrays arranged in the usual stacks, fits snugly into a little blue box no larger than a bedside radio set. Other machines have memory units containing millions of bits, or millions of cores. (For an historical comparison, ENIAC's vacuum-tube memory contained about six hundred bits.)

Notice that the cores of a memory unit have fixed positions within the system of piled-up arrays. A particular core might be located at row No. 5 and column No. 63 of the fourth array from the bottom, which corresponds roughly to saying that a person lives at 5 West 63rd Street on the fourth floor. In short, bits of information have precise addresses which may be referred to many, many times during the course of a long program. Furthermore, communications take place swiftly inside modern machines. The access time of a magnetic-core memory is measured in millionths of a second. That is, it takes only a few millionths of a second to extract a specific number or instruction from a specific address.

So far we have discussed the input, arithmetic, and memory units of the computer system. That leaves the control unit, which we shall save for last since it coordinates the workings of the entire system—and the output unit, which enables the machine to communicate its results to investigators. The answer to a problem, that is, a problem worth bringing to the machine's attention in the first place, is usually a series of numbers rather than a single number. The new information generated in the computer is transmitted in the form of the usual pulses representing binary digits. It may be relayed directly to an automatic device which punches a set of cards or a tape similar to that carrying the original program. Then the material is fed into an electric typewriter designed to translate patterns of holes into printed letters and decimal digits. This is simply the reverse of the input process.

Another type of unit presents more dynamic and vivid displays. At the beginning of Chapter 1 we mentioned an investigator watching a television-type screen or cathode-ray tube, one of the output devices of the TX-o computer. This particular investigator happened to be studying sound patterns produced during ordinary speech. But it might just as well have been any phenomenon involving change— the varying forces among atomic particles, the stresses on part of the wing of a jet plane, the path of a hurricane, the ups and downs of a business cycle. In any case, a computer may present a continuous "televised" record of its findings, a kind of running commentary about what is going on. Electrical pulses representing information can be made to direct the motions of a narrow beam of electrons which traces patterns on a fluorescent screen just as a pencil writes on paper. The patterns indicate changes that are of interest to investigators.

Now we are ready to describe a computer in action. Assume that a complete program has been fed into the machine and transferred to the memory unit. The information sits and waits in magnetic cores—until the calculating begins. Then the executive, the control unit, takes command. To direct the operations of a large-scale electronic device, it has a long list of responsibilities. The individual circuits in a computer, like the individual nerve cells in a brain, may be relatively simple. But there are a great many circuits and the way they have been hooked up or organized is far from simple.

Computers are probably the most elaborate machines ever built. Taking the number of parts as one index of complexity, consider an important research and development machine being used at a leading American laboratory. It has 35,000 transistors and roughly 350,000 other parts ("roughly" because no one has ever bothered to count them). Furthermore, this figure does not include the 2,500,000 magnetic cores in its memory unit. These parts are wired together into a single calculating system, a network of numerous pathways. Placed at strategic intersections and crossroads along the pathways are electronic gates, or switches, which serve to clear or block off routes within the network. An investigator has commented as follows on the complexity of such systems: "No one man knows the entire blueprint of any large-scale computer, and certainly no one man knows whether or not it is actually wired according to that blueprint."

The control unit is master of this maze. An instruction specifying that information is to flow from the arithmetic unit to the output unit, for example, calls for a series of timed steps. Certain routes must be established and others disconnected. Pulse signals must be transmitted through the system to open and close appropriate gates. The control unit sets up these operations, monitors the course of subsequent events, and performs additional duties—all in millionths of a second. It can be compared to a telephone operator, or rather a group of telephone operators, working full time at the controls of a superswitchboard.

A simple problem will indicate how the system works in practice. Suppose you want to add 239,897 and 695,436, and then multiply the sum by 443. First you write a program including the numbers and instructions, each of which is translated into holes on a paper tape and fed into its own memory address, or "register." The problem requires eight such registers. The numbers go into three registers which we shall call X, Y, and Z; the instructions go into registers A, B, C, D, and E. (An actual program uses numbers to indicate memory locations, but we are using letters to avoid confusion.) Here is a sample program to indicate what the machine must be told:

Instruction Register		Number Register
A	LDF	X
B	ADD	Y
C	MPY	Z
D	PRT	
E	HLT	

When you push the START button, the control unit is already connected so that it receives patterns of electrical pulses representing the instruction in register A. These pulses are coded signals which say, in effect, "go to register X and put the information you find at that location into the arithmetic unit." ("LDF" is shorthand for "load from," that is, transfer from memory to arithmetic unit.) So the control unit disconnects itself from register A and establishes a pathway to register X, extracting the number there (239,897). It also establishes another pathway to the register which contains the *next* instruction, register B—thus executing one step and preparing for the subsequent step simultaneously.

But no information passes along this pathway yet. That happens after the control unit, which is in effect serving as an electronic metronome and "beating time" throughout the entire program, completes its first instruction. At the proper moment it sends pulses to register B and extracts the "ADD Y" order. The order tells it to establish a pathway to a new location, storage register Y, extract the number 695,436, and add it to the number already in the arithmetic unit. That completes the first stage of the calculation.

Then the control unit communicates with the set of magnetic cores which holds its next instruction, register C. It is referred to number register Z from which it takes 443 and directs the carrying out of the last MPY, or "multiply," calculation. The PRT step tells it to set up a pathway from the arithmetic unit to the output unit and print the answer; the final step, HLT, instructs the control unit to put a halt to operations. The entire sequence of operations, of course, is finished in far less time than it takes to describe what happens. The calculations would require less than a hundredth of a second on one of the electronic computers in widespread use, and perhaps one-twentieth of that time on the fastest machines.

The main point of the above example is to show that there is nothing complicated about any individual operation. The complexity is a matter of the quantity and intensity of detail in both design and program. Computers can do many things which deserve our attention and respect. They can solve mathematical equations, direct the motions of machine tools, imitate certain functions of the human brain, help in the design of new computers. They can play good checkers and interesting chess. These and other applications will be described in later chapters—and all of them involve exactly the same sort of operations and exactly the same sort of circuits which we have already considered. It is not done with mirrors or magic, but with pieces of electronic hardware and the right programs of instructions.

In contrast to our sample program, actual programs call for a great deal more than adding, multiplying, and so on. You can instruct a machine to make decisions, to choose between different courses of action. For example, it can make a comparison after it has completed a particular calculation. If the number is greater than a certain value, the computer may proceed to the next in its series of instructions. If the number is less than the standard value, the computer may skip one or more instructions and follow out another part of the program. Furthermore, the same sequence of operations may be performed over and over again on different sets of numbers forming a so-called "loop" of instructions. Every efficient program is a complex of loops and loops-within-loops, and if things become too complex (as they usually do), investigators use special flow charts to help them figure out just what is supposed to happen when.

In carrying out a given program, the computer executes a great many operations over and above the ones already described. For example, it is continually writing notes to itself, filing them away, referring to them, and throwing them out. Any series of calculations produces a host of intermediate numbers which are needed in arriving at final answers but are no good afterward. You have roughly the same problem in filling out your income-tax form. You must wade through various calculations the results of which do not appear on the form. You may use a scratch pad to jot down the calculations and answers. When the tax return is completed, the paper ends up in the wastebasket.

A computer behaves in an analogous fashion. The routes between the memory unit and the arithmetic unit are not one-way routes, and the traffic of information going both ways is particularly heavy. The machine stores intermediate numbers, numbers of temporary interest only, in vacant memory locations. Or else it may erase numbers which have served their purposes and substitute new numbers. In either case, the memory unit may be used as a sort of scratch pad. It is a place for storing "transient" information as well as instructions and basic data.

The machine also has access to information located outside its memory unit. In many laboratories you can see upright glass-enclosed cabinets each containing two reels of magnetic tape. As the tape unwinds from one reel, it winds onto the other. The action is something like that of the ribbon on a typewriter or the film in a motion-picture projector—with one difference. The tape does not unwind continuously from one reel to the other. The reels spin in one direction, stop, rotate a quarter of a turn in the reverse direction, stop, reverse direction again, and so on.

The computer is referring to an external memory, "thumbing through" a book whose pages contain magnetic spots instead of letters. During the course of solving a problem, it looks up sines and cosines, logarithms, and other numbers which mathematicians have arranged in tables. These tables are used in solving many different problems, but the computer's built-in memory is not large enough to hold all of them. So the machine does what any human computer would do when he needs information not stored in his head—it looks up the information in a library. At the proper times its control unit sets up pathways to the library, which, incidentally, may also include instructions prepared for other problems and applicable to the current problem as well. Racks filled with reels testify to the fact that libraries for machines are growing as rapidly as libraries for human readers.

Computers have come a long way during the past decade. Among other things, they can do considerably more than early models, operate at greater speeds, and have larger memories. Yet there is room for improvement, not only in the design of the machine itself but also in the way we use it. Take the problem of machine errors, for example. Although modern computers are not nearly as unpredictable as their ancestors, they continue to act up from time to time. Only in science fiction can robot brains operate for ages or forever without the need of mere human beings. The machines among us today do not run on their own; they require the presence of trained attendants.

On the average the computing units of a large-scale machine can be expected to make some sort of error once every month or so. We would hardly be satisfied with such a performance record in our television sets, washing machines, or car engines. In the case of computers, however, there are extenuating circumstances. For one thing, when a machine performs tens of thousands of operations a second, it can do so much in several hours of running time that we can excuse its failures. For another, various routines have been worked out which make it possible to keep things in good working order for better than 80 per cent of the time. If you are ready for an error, and if you can find it and fix it quickly, then troubleshooting need not be a major problem.

This is how things have worked out. We have learned to live with our temperamental machines and take errors in stride. A standard practice is the morning checkup, which may last an hour or two. When a doctor wants to check the condition of your heart, he will ask you to exert yourself for a brief period—say, by jumping up and down on one foot. The exercise puts a small extra load on the heart and helps the doctor detect potential trouble. Engineers have developed similar "exercise" programs which put computers to the test by making them perform special operations. Such techniques generally reveal the presence of loose wires, weak tubes, and other sources of trouble.

Also, the machine can be made to assist engineers and check itself. One way involves the use of circuits which count the 1's in every stored number. For example, take the binary expression 11001110. You allow an extra place, an extra memory core, which reads "0" if the number of 1's is even and "1" if the number of 1's is odd. Thus this number might be placed in the memory unit as 11001110-1. Every time the number is extracted from or replaced into the memory, the control unit checks it automatically. If a 1 has changed to a 0 or a 0 to a 1, the machine stops dead in its tracks and an alarm bell rings. (Notice that two such errors occurring at the same time in the same number would not be detected. But the chances of encountering this kind of double trouble are slim.) Patterns of neon lights on a panel indicate where the trouble lies and help speed up the repair process.

Incidentally, there is a way of insuring practically error-proof operation, if you can afford the price of two computers. One machine, the monitor, is instructed to keep tabs on the other, to "watch out" for absurd or unreasonable answers. It carries a complete picture of what is going on in the other machine and, in case of trouble, will take over all calculations at the flick of a switch. This two-heads-are-better-than-one approach is used in the SAGE air defense system and other strategically important installations. Under ordinary circumstances, testing routines do a more than adequate job, and improved parts are certain to come with further research.

It might be pointed out that a measure of humility is in order at this stage. We are not in exactly the best possible position to criticize machines. Like some parents with their children, we tend to set higher standards for them than we do for ourselves. And the matter of errors is a case in point. To be sure, computers make mistakes and make them far more frequently than many investigators would like. Until future developments we shall have to resign ourselves and be content with present performance levels—which happen to be notably superior to human performance levels.

The sort of errors we have been discussing involve flaws among the machine's several hundred thousand parts. Compare such troubles with the problem described at the beginning of this chapter, the case of the computer that ran wild. In that case there was nothing wrong with the machine itself. Its vacuum tubes were in first-rate condition, its wiring connections intact. In undertaking the impossible task of dividing by zero, it was simply obeying orders—and the mistake in those orders was a human not an electronic mistake. When this case occurred, the electronic type of flaw was perhaps more common than it is today.

As things stand now, the betting odds are distinctly in favor of the machine. In fact, when an inspection reveals that something is wrong with the answers being provided by the output unit, the trouble most likely lies with the man rather than with the machine. The first thing you do in such a case is re-examine the program which the investigator has written out. You will probably find an average of one man-made mistake or so for every hundred instructions and, considering that programs may include thousands of instructions, this represents a respectable number of errors.

Furthermore, and this is perhaps the insult supreme, we depend on the machine to help us locate our slipups. The best way to detect the flaws in a program is to run it through a computer, piece by piece, in a process known as "debugging." Finding and correcting errors may be more difficult than writing out the program in the first place, and it often takes more of the machine's expensive time than the actual problem. Clearly if a machine were capable of expressing exasperation, we should be tempted to alter its wiring diagram. A recent report contains a word of timely advice: "Professional programmers are accustomed to their own fallibility . . . but the casual amateur is more optimistic, brashly supposing that he is the master of the machine, rather than the reverse."

Speaking of professional programmers, the demand for such experts is steadily on the rise. In 1953 there were some two thousand programming specialists in the United States, and the number increased tenfold during the next three years. Today the total is probably about a hundred thousand, and it will continue to increase with the coming of more computers. Programmers spend their time as middlemen in the flow of information from man to machine. They are interpreters of a sort, and one aim of current research is to make their jobs simpler by improving methods of communicating with the machines.

We need new languages which will be more "natural" for us and, among other things, help reduce errors. Unless we can speak with computers more easily, we shall continue to be plagued by mistakes of our own making. At one time investigators had no choice but to use the language of the machine. ENIAC, the first electronic computer, was also the first (and the last) to be based on the decimal system. So instructions were written out in a straight number language, in decimal digits. For instance, 792 and 438 might represent "add" and "multiply" respectively. In binary computers combinations of 0's and 1's served the same purpose.

It is no longer necessary to speak numbers to machines, to express instructions in an unnatural and time-consuming numerical notation. To take a simple example, suppose you want to tell a computer to stop if the sum of two numbers,

A and B, is greater than a certain total C. In one old-style machine language this would have to be written and then typed out as follows:

$$
\begin{array}{llll}
0 & 0000 & 10 & 1000 \\
0 & 0000 & 12 & 1001 \\
0 & 0000 & 18 & 2000 \\
0 & 0000 & 34 & 2050 \\
\end{array}
$$

Now you simply write and type "IF $A + B > 0$ THEN GO TO HALT." (The ">" is standard algebraic shorthand for "is greater than.")

This expression is written in ALGOL, an algebraic language devised by an international group especially for programs used in solving mathematical problems. Many other synthetic language systems have been developed for talking to electronic machines, and each one of them has its synthetic name. IBM investigators prepared FORTRAN (Formula Translation) to deal with numerical operations. There is a system known as COBOL (Common Business Oriented Language) to help in the writing out of programs concerning such matters as payroll calculations and inventory control and depreciation records. Economists are interested in using machines to analyze and predict business trends, and for this purpose M.I.T. investigators have designed DYNAMO (Dynamic Model). COMIT, also developed at M.I.T., is designed for experimental programs involving automatic translation.

Synthetic languages ease the job of communicating with computers. But, again, we have to call on the computers themselves for assistance. In converting from a synthetic language—say, COBOL—to binary terms, the machine must play two roles. First it serves purely as a translator. It may receive a punched tape written in COBOL and perform the series of operations required to spell out the same instructions in its own binary language. The result is the production of another tape, the working tape. It may be inserted into the input unit of the machine, which, now playing the role of problem-solver, proceeds with its calculations.

Notice what is happening during such procedures. Instead of having to translate his program into pure machine language, the investigator uses a language which has certain elements in common with his own and which he can learn readily. He shifts a large part of the translating task to the machine. In other words, the machine helps him to put his instructions into terms that it can understand. It also permits the investigator to write out fewer and less detailed instructions, which means that he makes fewer errors. Another result is that programs which took two months to prepare using previous methods can now be completed in four or five days.

On the other hand, we have not yet reached the most desirable state of affairs. We cannot yet use the King's English and talk easily with machines the way we often do with one another. There is still a certain awkwardness or formality in our communications. But the trend is increasingly toward what are known as "problem-oriented languages," which are closely related to our native tongues —and further and further away from "machine-oriented languages," which express instructions by means of numbers. The goal is conversation, the free give-and-take exchange of ideas which occurs when investigators discuss complicated design projects with one another.

There is another serious communications problem which concerns computer speeds. It happens that the machines are so fast that everything we do seems hopelessly slow and wasteful by comparison. Suppose the investigator has to answer a phone call just before inserting a taped program into a computer. The phone call may take only three minutes, but in that time a modern computer may perform about twenty million operations. Or suppose the investigator, using the latest methods, breaks all previous programming records. He manages to write out a full and errorless set of instructions in three days—and the machine comes up with the answer in two or three minutes. It is something like taking a day's hike to an airport and catching a jet plane that will take you halfway across the country in less than three hours.

Of course, we can alleviate this situation somewhat by building up a large backlog of programs ready to feed into the computer at a moment's notice. The basic difficulty still remains, however. Furthermore, backlogs will not take care of another problem involving the mismatch between man and machine. Not long ago a physicist put a problem to a computer and received the information he wanted in four minutes. But the computer's arithmetic unit was not operating all that time. It was actually loafing for more than three minutes, waiting while other units and sluggish investigators went about their business. Three minutes may not seem like much, but in that loafing period the machine could have done the work of a man spending a year at a desk calculator.

Ways of coping more effectively with the mismatch problem are under active study. One plan is to have the computer serve a number of investigators at once, by giving them brief but valuable fragments of its time in rapid succession. Like a chess master playing games against many opponents and going from board to board, the machine shifts its attention from problem to problem. The chess master, to be sure, has a simpler task in one sense. After all, he is playing chess only. The machine may be at work on entirely different types of "games." It may be analyzing financial statements, the life history of a star, the results of a national election or census, the design of a jet-plane wing, and the arrangements of atoms in giant molecules.

As soon as it is finished with a set of calculations for problem No. 1, it switches to problem No. 2, then to the next problem, and so on. It is continually on the move.

This system, known as time-sharing, is still being developed. It depends among other things on the design of new kinds of input-output devices and the more efficient design and use of computer languages. But it is coming. In fact, the next year or two will see the increased application of time-sharing—and a spurt in efforts to solve some extremely difficult problems which are not being pushed at top speed right now. It will not be long before machines will work with ten investigators in shifts, while even larger groups of perhaps as many as a hundred will be involved in the more distant future.

We have attained a certain measure of efficiency in communicating with one another. But no single investigator or group of investigators could possibly speak fast enough or long enough to keep a fast computer busy full time. Until we find a method of preparing complete and precise programs at far greater speeds, we shall need time-sharing or something like it. And if a lightning programmer ever appears, it will certainly not be a man but a new species of computer.

MATHEMATICS AND LOGIC

COMPUTERS ARE TOOLS designed for the sole purpose of dealing with complexity, with masses of detailed information from any source. You can measure their value in many ways. The Chesapeake and Ohio Railroad has been using a Univac to analyze its schedules and recently saved some $900,000 by routing existing freight cars more efficiently instead of buying new ones. More money is flowing into the United States Treasury as computers take over much of the job of keeping tabs on our income statements. For example, they digest facts about bank accounts and investments and check the information with what is reported, and unreported, on individual tax returns. As a result of this checking operation alone, the Internal Revenue Service expects to collect about four billion dollars a year which it is not collecting now.

Every time a new satellite is put into orbit, scientists and military officials and communications engineers must cope with vast quantities of new data. The data are flashed through space in the form of coded messages, signals radioed to the ground by electronic telemetering devices. There is far more information in these signals than the brain can possibly handle without automatic thinking aids.

In a single passage around the earth a single reconnaissance satellite could take enough photographs, and cover territory in such minute detail, that it would require 100 million intelligence experts to analyze all the observations.

Computers must do the analyzing in these and a great many other cases. They must solve extremely difficult mathematical equations, abstract descriptions of physical problems expressed in symbolic shorthand—and as the problems become more and more complicated, the equations describing them also become more and more complicated. It may not be possible to predict the course of human evolution during the next century or two, but one thing is clear. We seem to be determined to go faster and further and higher. Increasing numbers of investigators are working on plans for voyages of exploration in outer space and are encountering a variety of strange phenomena, the understanding and control of which depend on the use of calculating machines.

One class of phenomena in particular presents a challenge to design engineers in many fields. A number of years ago a large rocket rose from its launching pad at the White Sands Missile Range in New Mexico, started to pick up speed, and seemed well on the way to a normal flight. Suddenly things began to go wrong. The first sign of real trouble was a cloud of smoke and a terrific noise, a piercing high-pitched whistle that increased in intensity. Then the rocket faltered as a jet of fire burst through its side. Metal walls crumpled like paper, and it fell back to earth.

This sort of failure, known as "screaming," is a common ailment of experimental rockets and missiles. It has been traced to a peculiar type of instability set up inside the combustion chambers of rocket motors, where the burning of more than 6 tons of fuel a minute may generate energy at a rate a hundred times faster than that required to keep the liner *Queen Elizabeth* running at full speed. Screaming may occur when gas pressures rise suddenly. This causes fuel to burn faster and further increases the pressure so that the flow of fuel into the chamber is effectively blocked or cut down sharply.

Then the reaction sets in. Reduced fuel flow brings about slower burning, a drop in pressure—and a spurt of fresh fuel which leads to another jump in burning rates and pressures, another reduction of incoming fuel, and so on. The result may be a self-sustaining process, a cycle which mounts in intensity and builds up stronger and stronger reverberations. Seething hot gases begin to pulse as many as five thousand times a second, creating pressure waves like those which produce notes in organ pipes. But the music inside rockets is unwanted music, and although engineers can modify design features so as to eliminate screaming during the course of developing a specific rocket, each new rocket presents a new risk of wall-shattering pressure waves.

Problems of a similar nature crop up in supersonic aircraft. Major surprises rarely occur at speeds of a few hundred miles an hour; the aerodynamics of low-speed flight are well worked out. For one thing, it has long been known that planes move in a kind of skin or sheath of dead air. The skin, which is called the boundary layer and may be several inches thick, clings to surfaces like a film and generally stays put.

But no one is settling for a few hundred miles an hour these days. Increase the speed and abrupt changes take place. The boundary layer begins to act up. It may peel off a wing surface, flutter and flap about like a flag in the breeze, and give rise to high-energy shock waves. All at once smooth-flowing air becomes turbulent and breaks into vortices, producing strong vibrations in thin wings. Wing flaps and other parts that are movable under normal conditions may lock fast or freeze in position.

Similar effects have accounted for a number of air tragedies. Not long after World War II Geoffrey de Haviland, one of England's ace pilots, lost his life when vibrations shook his plane to pieces in mid-flight. About five years ago, high over the Edwards Air Force Base in California's Mojave Desert, an experimental plane was performing in spectacular fashion. For one brief period, under perfect control, it reached a speed unprecedented in those days— more than 2,000 miles an hour. In the next instant certain structural limits were exceeded. The plane changed from a flawlessly operating machine to a thing gone wild. It began shuddering and bucking and twisting, spun into a long spiral dive, and crashed on the desert in flames.

The problem is not confined to airplanes and rockets. During the summer of 1940 the third largest suspension bridge in the world—the Narrows Bridge in Tacoma, Washington—was opened to traffic. One morning some four months later the structure started vibrating in mild-gale winds up to 42 miles an hour. Its slender roadway twisted like a ribbon of confetti along its full length, and soon afterward plunged into Puget Sound. The bridge had literally shaken itself to pieces. Since then the danger has been caught in time in many other cases. For example, in 1953 engineers spent more than $3,000,000 to stiffen structural members of San Francisco's Golden Gate Bridge.

Here is an excerpt from a report on the Tacoma disaster: "[The bridge] was adequately safe for all of the loads and forces for which it had been designed, namely dead load, live load, temperature and the static effect of wind load. . . . Thus the Tacoma span was the victim of its extreme flexibility and of the vulnerability of its cross section to the creation of resultant wind forces producing cumulative amplification of oscillations." In other words, winds exerted a lifting action on the flat roadway as if it were an airplane wing, setting up larger and larger vibrations which shattered the bridge.

Electronic devices also fail because of related effects. The currents flowing in defective vacuum tubes can set up self-sustaining oscillations, and when that happens radios may howl and snow appears on television screens. Radar devices designed to track fast-moving planes and missiles have been known to break down so that instead of following their targets, they go into a vibratory, back-and-forth movement like a palsied hand. All such phenomena are examples of a basic vulnerability in complex systems, a tendency to develop malignant oscillations under certain conditions. The tendency has always existed, but it is aggravated as engineers subject machines and structures to increasingly severe stresses.

Mathematical expressions suitable for dealing with a large number of these problems were developed long before the need for them became critical. During the 1880's the great French mathematician Henri Poincaré studied certain "nonlinear" equations involving periodic functions whose values may have a repeating or oscillating quality. He was concerned primarily with basic studies and had no way of knowing that his findings would be applied to the analysis of engineering problems. Incidentally, one of his contemporaries, the Russian A. Liapounoff, did similar work, and Russian mathematicians have long been leaders in research along these lines.

This broad area of mathematics also includes equations which help in the study of situations where oscillations are not the cause of trouble. Investigators use nonlinear equations to analyze the breaking of highly stressed steel girders and springs, the explosion of compressed gases, the deformation of metals subjected to high temperatures in missiles and space vehicles and nuclear power plants. Engineers are designing things closer and closer to the breaking point, systems which operate just barely on the safe side of catastrophe and sometimes exceed their limits.

Nonlinear equations are often extremely difficult to solve. In fact, some of them are so forbidding that no investigator in his right mind would even have considered tackling them ten or fifteen years ago. There is little point in calling on our imaginary man at a desk calculator to indicate how long it would take to solve such equations without the new computers. He would die of old age on the job, assuming that boredom did not claim him sooner, and enough work would still remain to keep many succeeding generations of human calculators occupied on a full-time basis.

The electronic computer cannot handle nonlinear equations in their original form. But they can be written out in simpler terms, expanded into long expressions involving repeated combinations of four familiar operations: addition, subtraction, multiplication, and division. The process is something like explaining things to a child, or translating the highly condensed jargon of technical reports into plain English which laymen can understand. Given information in sufficiently elementary terms, computers can take the problem from there in. As has been pointed out, their arithmetic circuits are built to operate at enormous speeds and perform long series of routine calculations automatically.

But certain nonlinear equations tax the fullest powers of the fastest computers. Consider equations describing the behavior of electrically charged atomic particles moving in magnetic fields. Such particles are believed to produce radio signals coming from supernovae or exploded stars and from colliding galaxies located near the very edge of the observable universe. They are associated with sunspots and other solar disturbances which create magnetic storms in the upper atmosphere and may garble long-distance communications.

Current efforts to control hydrogen-bomb energies in thermonuclear furnaces depend on how effectively investigators can control the motions of charged particles—and if the efforts succeed, enough energy will become available to meet all mankind's demands for the next million years. These problems and many others on the frontiers of scientific research involve equations which, when expressed in computer terms, call for billions of arithmetic operations. For such tasks we need all the calculating speed we can get.

It should be emphasized that even when computers do not yield results of immediate practical value, they may help extend our knowledge of basic processes. Investigators are just beginning to use the machines for the study of screaming and similar rocket phenomena which are responsible for failures and may account for some of the delays encountered during the drive to produce larger and more powerful rockets. Indeed, some mathematicians have suggested that Soviet advances in the mathematics of nonlinear equations may be one reason for the fact that we are lagging in certain aspects of the space race.

Weather research is another area in which computers are helping investigators to understand, if not yet to solve, problems of great complexity. No one needs to be reminded that accurate prediction is still more of an art than a science. Daily weather reports are not always as reliable as they might be. We have all heard television and radio forecasters explaining why the 4 to 8 inches of snow they predicted yesterday failed to fall as scheduled, or why a blizzard came despite the absence of advance warnings. The weatherman's fate is that his failures are remembered far more vividly than his successes.

If you must have a scapegoat, however, blame the innate cussedness of nature. Equations applicable to the analysis of weather phenomena are nonlinear with a vengeance, which is another way of saying that things may happen suddenly and we have little idea why. What do we have to know about the physical conditions in a great body of air so that we can tell in advance whether or not it will develop into a hurricane? Why does the jet stream, a system of high-speed winds flowing miles above the earth's surface, suddenly veer in its course like a meandering river? Such questions must be answered precisely before meteorologists can predict when storms and other disturbances will occur, and what paths they will follow.

Glowing reports to the contrary, notable advances in long-range weather forecasting are still a development for the future. At present many investigators are using computers not to predict weather, but to attain a better understanding of the atmosphere as a whole. Programs of instructions and numbers specify the sort of equations involved and the weather data which must be rearranged to satisfy the equations. Already the machines have provided insights into the eccentricities of vast air masses, for example, into the nature of turbulence which may appear suddenly and produce unstable conditions as well as changes in the paths of storms. In other words, computers are playing a role in providing the basic information upon which, in the last analysis, improved weather prediction depends.

The problems considered up to this point all require ordinary arithmetic operations, work with numbers. But the machines can also be used to work with certain types of ideas, to simplify and analyze the consistency of statements. This brings us to another important area of mathematics, logic, and to a man who has been described as follows: "He has a strong claim to the sour honor of having been the most greatly underrated mathematician of the nineteenth century. Self-taught, [he] lacked the alleged advantages of an orthodox training in the mathematics of his time. His originality was so aggressive that it might have overcome even the thorough education which he regretted having missed through poverty."

In 1854 George Boole, an English schoolteacher, published his masterpiece, *An Investigation of the Laws of
Thought*. He invented a symbolic logic, a kind of algebra
of ideas in which *x*'s and *y*'s stand for statements rather
than numbers, and special signs stand for "or," "and," "if
. . . then," and other relationships among statements. As
far as computers are concerned, the significant thing about
his mathematical language is that it represents what is
known as a two-valued logic. That is, it deals with statements that are either true or false. Thus, if *x* stands for
"kittens love fish," $\bar{x}$ (shorthand for "not *x*") stands for
"kittens do not love fish."

This simple feature of two-valued logic fits in beautifully
with the basic operation of computers. In fact, Boole could
have performed no greater service to designers if he had
been thinking specifically of the machines when he devised
his "laws of thought." There is a neat and direct relation-
ship between two-valued logic and the binary system, the
natural computer language. Since the binary digits 0 and
1 can stand for "false" and "true," respectively, a computer
can be used to solve logical as well as numerical problems.
If the binary expression 111 represents the statement "kittens love fish," then 111-0 could mean the statement is
false and 111-1 that it is true.

Logical problems involve relationships of varying degrees
of complexity among different statements. Here is a simple
example taken from a textbook on logic written by the
English mathematician Charles Dodgson, who, writing
under the pseudonym Lewis Carroll, was the author of
Alice's Adventures in Wonderland. One and only one conclusion can be deduced from the following statements:

No kitten that loves fish is unteachable.
No kitten without a tail will play with a gorilla.
Kittens with whiskers always love fish.

No teachable kitten has green eyes.
No kittens have tails unless they have whiskers.

One way of solving this puzzle is to express the statements in the algebraic terms of symbolic logic.

C. R. Wylie, Jr., of the University of Utah offers a somewhat more difficult puzzle. One of four men—Archie, Dave, Gus, and Tony—is known to have committed a certain crime. Under questioning by the police they give conflicting testimony. According to Archie, "Dave committed the crime." Dave said, "Tony is the guilty one." Gus named no one, but claimed, "I am innocent." Tony's only comment was, "Dave lied when he said I did it." Now assuming that one and only one of the four statements of the suspects is true, who was the guilty man?

Of course, it is not necessary to use a formal mathematical approach in dealing with these puzzles. Straight reasoning without the benefit of symbols is sufficient for relatively simple systems of statements. For example, the answer to the Lewis Carroll problem becomes evident after you reword the statements and put them in the right order:

Green-eyed kittens cannot be taught.
Kittens that cannot be taught do not love fish.
Kittens that do not love fish have no whiskers.
Kittens that have no whiskers have no tails.
Kittens that have no tails will not play with a gorilla.

The one valid deduction, then, is that green-eyed kittens will not play with a gorilla.

Small machines have been built which can solve problems of this sort and do some of the tedious work required in courses on logic. We cannot afford to bother an electronic computer with such trivial matters. But there are logical problems worthy of the machine, and more and more of them will arise as society becomes more and more complex. For example, think of the legal paper work involved in the normal course of current events. We have contracts between large industrial companies and governments, contracts between these companies and smaller companies, increasing numbers of municipal and state and Federal laws, union-management contracts, leases and deeds and agreements and purchase orders. A single contract or law may include many many pages of fine print, many *if*'s and *and*'s and *but*'s, many loopholes, and perhaps conflicting clauses.

The effort to avoid inconsistencies and provide for all eventualities may become too much for the most perceptive legal minds. The first attempt to apply symbolic logic to such problems was made more than twenty-five years ago when a mathematician, Edmund Berkeley of the Prudential Life Insurance Company, discovered a conflict between two statements in a lengthy document stipulating policies for premium payments. Since then there have been other attempts to wade through formidable legal documents with the aid of mathematical logic.

So far the complexities of the problems have not demanded the extensive use of computers. But you can be sure that the time is coming. The rise of the megapolis, densely populated urban areas extending for hundreds of miles, will bring a sharp rise in the number and complexity of zoning and construction laws. There are new agreements among new countries, new and more elaborate international laws of all sorts, new laws involving the rights and duties of nations exploring space. Sooner or later we are certain to reach a point where only computers can cope with the most intricate mazes of legal terminology.

At present perhaps the most fruitful applications of symbolic logic are in engineering. In this area an outstanding contributor has been Claude Shannon of M.I.T., a mathematical investigator known internationally for his original

Claude Shannon—pioneer in the application of logic to computer design and theory.

work on a wide variety of basic research problems. More than twenty years ago, when he was still a student in the Institute's Department of Electrical Engineering, Shannon completed what must certainly be one of the most distinguished theses ever written for a master's degree. Presented in clear and straightforward terms, it described for the first time how Boolean algebra, or symbolic logic, could be used in the mathematical analysis of "circuits designed to perform complex operations automatically."

To illustrate the general idea of this approach, consider the following electrical circuit:

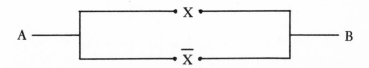

The two switches are labelled X and $\overline{X}$ (not X) to indicate that they are connected in such a way that when one is open the other is closed. When current flows from A toward B, it has two possible pathways—and, since one of the switches is always closed, one of the pathways is always available to complete the circuit. This is a "redundant" circuit, which means that the two switches are logically unnecessary and the same result, one available pathway, may be achieved with a simple wire:

A •———————————————————————————• B

Shannon's study makes it possible, among other things, to examine circuits and simplify them if they have too many components. As a first step you translate the circuit and its open-closed switches into an expression or equation made up of logical true-false (1 or 0) statements. If the circuit has extra switches, you will be able to simplify the equation, get rid of the extra terms, and then translate the new equation back into a more economical circuit. For example, such an analysis readily shows that the two following circuits perform exactly the same function:

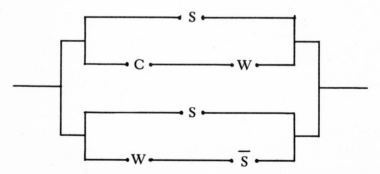

The six-switch circuit above may be replaced by the circuit below having only two switches.

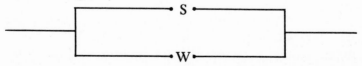

When things really get complicated, computers are used to analyze and simplify circuits. There are circuit diagrams which cover many pages, resembling nightmare labyrinths in their complexity—and it is here that the machines come to our rescue by doing symbolic logic instead of arithmetic. Special programs including the rules of two-valued logic and details of the problem to be solved are fed into the memory unit. Computers then proceed to carry out their instructions. After performing numerous logical operations, they type out the specifications for simpler and more efficient circuits.

Electronic logic may bring about appreciable savings in systems made up of a great many elementary circuits—and the systems are being manufactured in greater and greater quantities. Computers help design long-range rockets like those used for military purposes and for launching satellites and planet-bound vehicles. The rockets contain elaborate devices so that they can be steered, either directly and automatically or by remote control from the ground. Other devices measure conditions in space and send back information by radio. All this requires considerable circuitry. According to the recent statement of an Army research director, for example, "the inside of an ICBM [intercontinental ballistic missile] makes the back of your television set look as simple as apple pie."

Wherever you find such complexity, it is a good bet that engineers have called on the services of logic-performing computers. Automatic ship and airplane pilots, airport traffic-control centers, radar networks—these and many other systems may include hundreds or thousands of electronic switches, vacuum tubes, and transistors. The Bell Telephone Laboratories have set up on an experimental basis the world's first electronic telephone exchange. Located in Morris, Illinois, in the farm-belt region seventy-five miles southwest of Chicago, it incorporates many new features. You can get in touch with people you phone often more easily than with people you phone only now and then, by dialing only two instead of seven numbers. Or say you are going out for the evening. If you expect important calls, you can dial a code which will route them to the number of the home you are visiting. If a number is busy, you can hang up with the reassuring knowledge that the central office will automatically ring you back as soon as the line is free.

Furthermore, the electronic exchange continually checks up on its circuits. If something is wrong, it locates and diagnoses the trouble. In some cases it can even correct the flaw, say, by shifting from a faulty to an intact circuit or channel. In all other cases it promptly communicates with the outside world. One unit of the exchange describes the trouble on a teletype machine, and from there in human technicians take over the repair work. To perform these and other duties, the new system requires 12,000 transistors and more than 100,000 vacuum tubes.

There is no unwanted redundancy in its circuits. The system is the result of long-range research which started during the 1930's, and symbolic logic played an important part in its design. Shannon spent more than ten years at the Laboratories developing ideas originally conceived in his classic master's-degree thesis. The thesis, by the way, included much more than has been indicated so far. For one thing, it went considerably beyond the simplification of existing circuits. It showed how a two-valued logic can be used in starting from scratch, in creating completely new circuits designed according to precise specifications.

The paper also pointed the way to a most meaningful development and one which illustrates in a particularly striking way the potentialities of computers. If a computer can be used to help design the circuits of rocket devices and many more complex electronic systems, why not use

These racks of electronic equipment are part of a computer
at the Army's Ascension Island antimissile defense station.
The machine automatically tracks missiles in flight.

it to design the circuits of other computers? Not long ago
this notion seemed like an interesting but rather remote
possibility. Today it is standard practice in all creative design work from the construction of supplementary circuits
for existing machines to the planning of entirely new computers.

About a year ago Bell Laboratories investigators completed "the first computer ever built from complete information furnished · by another computer." The machine,
located on Ascension Island in the South Atlantic, was
developed in collaboration with Remington Rand experts
for tracking missiles launched from Cape Canaveral in
Florida. It is being used as part of the intricate communi-

Computer designs computer: electronic circuits for the missile-tracking computer on Ascension Island were designed with the aid of another computer—whose typed-out information is being read by Bell Telephone Laboratories engineer Gabe Sellers.

cations systems which provide defenses against enemy attacks, to guide the Army's Nike-Zeus missiles so that they will make direct hits on their targets—long-range intercontinental missiles.

The first step in building this machine was to write a "logic diagram," expressing pictorially the logical network which would enable the machine to perform its functions. Then the diagram was converted into fifty sets of special logical equations, or a total of several thousand equations in all. Each set represented a different subassembly, a combination of circuits which made up sections of the computer's arithmetic and control units. At this stage, however, the subassemblies existed only in the form of abstract logical statements which had to be translated into hardware, specific electronic parts. Another computer did the translating, solving the sets of equations on the basis of orders spelled out in programs of about thirty-seven thousand instructions.

This machine spent about twenty-five hours doing what would otherwise have taken a month or more. The result was a series of lists indicating all the parts required to build the Nike-Zeus computer, an impressive feat when you consider that its units include about ten thousand transistors and many more components. Not only that, but the lists produced what was in effect a full wiring diagram. They showed exactly how the parts should be connected to form complete circuits. Much of the assembly work was done by hand, but now the process has been further mechanized by a number of companies. Computer No. 1 turns out punched tapes or cards which are fed to computer No. 2, which in turn operates machines designed to assemble automatically the circuits for computer No. 3.

In another special project engineers at Remington Rand put one of their Univac models to work on a more advanced computer, known as Larc. This machine, originally built for the Atomic Energy Commission and now available commercially, has accomplished a number of impressive feats. One important problem involving reactions in a nuclear power plant, and the solution of some hair-raising nonlinear equations, had been resting on the shelf unsolved because it would have required five months to run on existing computers. Larc turned out a solution in a day and a half.

But speed is by no means its only unusual characteristic. It can do more with fewer basic circuits, and each one of these circuits has been simplified so that it is composed of a minimum number of electronic parts. The simplification process has been extended even further, to the point where the circuits are hooked together in the most compact and economical way possible. Univac spent fifty hours figuring out how Larc's circuits should be put together, and furnished a typed list of about sixty thousand wired connections. The result is a high order of operating efficiency. Things get done faster with fewer breakdowns, and considerably less time is required to make repairs.

The applications discussed in this chapter have all involved a three-stage procedure. What has usually happened is that pure mathematicians discover new and fruitful and highly abstract relationships. Then there is a time lag, which in the past has often been fifty years or more, before the new abstractions are put to use. (The time lag, incidentally, is tending to become shorter and shorter.) Scientists recognize that certain mathematical or logical equations can help them solve problems in basic or applied research. In the third and final stage, scientists may call on computers to take over the necessary calculations. There is no doubt where the computers stand in the mathematician-scientist-computer hierarchy. They are clearly underdogs, hardly more creative than file clerks in massive business or government organizations.

But it all depends on how you use them. The fact that they are performing limited services does not in any way imply that their capacities are correspondingly limited. Machines can help the investigator solve an equation which the mathematician has conceived. Can they also play a role, however humble, in the creative activities of pure mathematics? Some mathematicians think so. Eric Temple Bell of the California Institute of Technology, who wrote brilliantly about the history of mathematics and had a deep-seated distaste for computers, nevertheless made some concessions: "New calculating machines . . . multiply the efficiency of the individual mathematician (and sometimes also his ego) by a factor which may be as high as ten—he accomplishes ten times as much, when given the proper tools in the right kind of factory, as he would if working in polite penury and scholarly solitude." John von Neumann made a similar point shortly after the appearance of ENIAC: "Computers will aid pure mathematicians, particularly those whose work is held up all along the line by the nature of nonlinear problems."

To date, the machines have contributed much more to applied than to pure mathematics. But there are a number of studies which hint at future possibilities. A program which makes it possible for a large-scale computer to find proofs for mathematical theorems has been developed by Herbert Simon, Allen Newell, and J. Clifford Shaw of Pittsburgh's Carnegie Institute of Technology and the Rand Corporation in Santa Monica, California. The machine was given a number of theorems from Whitehead and Russell's *Principia Mathematica*, an inquiry into the logical foundations of mathematics, and instructed to find proofs of the theorems. In other words, the task was to find consistent sets of deductions leading to specific conclusions.

The machine managed to develop proofs of most of the theorems fed to it. Even more interesting, in one case it found a proof more elegant than that devised by the authors of the *Principia*. The secret of such work, of course, lies in the programs prepared for computers. Simon and his co-workers are not primarily concerned with pure mathematics but with instructing machines to solve problems the way we do. Their studies are part of an expanding area of research on "artificial intelligence," which will be considered in more detail later.

But judging by their results to date, Simon and Newell have made a bold prediction: "Within ten years . . . a computer will discover and prove an important new mathematical theorem." If their prediction turns out to be accurate, we do not have long to wait. It was made in 1957. In any case, the statement would have been regarded as sheer fantasy during the early days of computer technology, but we must take it seriously today.

But whatever happens in the future, right now is the time to put existing machines in proper perspective. According to the writings of some overly enthusiastic scientists and reporters, the millennium has already arrived. A general-purpose computer which solves equations and does logic and plays chess is capable of the highest type of thinking. It will not be long before it becomes more than a match for the brain itself. There is no telling what the future may bring. Perhaps we are rapidly coming closer to a time when machines will go berserk like Frankenstein's monster, or systematically take over the world like the factory-made revolutionists of R.U.R. (Rossum's Universal Robots), a fantasy by the Czech playwright Karel Čapek.

At the other extreme are unimpressed commentators who use words like "stupid," "slow-witted," and "moronic" to describe the electronic computer of today. It is essentially no more intelligent than a player piano which makes music according to patterns of perforations in rolls of paper and has never been known to add an unprogrammed note, much less to prepare an original composition. As for running our affairs, it cannot even handle its own operations without engineers and technicians to keep it in a state of good repair.

Bumbling computers lack the insight to recognize mistakes which would be obvious to the lowliest mortal. More than one factory worker has received a weekly paycheck for several million dollars or an unrealistically generous Christmas bonus, because something went wrong in the workings of computers. A computer figuring out marks at an Ohio university flunked about a dozen students who knew they had passed, demanded and got a recount, and were reinstated by an embarrassed administration.

Critics cite these and other boners to emphasize the limited status of current machines. For those who expect to rely increasingly on machines during the years ahead, they have a pointed joke. A group of passengers sat back in their seats as the giant transatlantic jet liner took off and started climbing. Suddenly they heard a clicking over the plane's loudspeaker system, a humming sound and a hollow, metallic voice: "This is a recording. Your flight is being controlled by the RS679 computer. There is no pilot and no crew. There are no stewardesses. But you have nothing to worry about. Everything has been checked thoroughly to insure your complete comfort. You are perfectly safe, perfectly safe, perfectly safe. . . ."

As is the case in most debates, the truth lies somewhere between the starry-eyed and skeptical attitudes and neither extreme does justice to the facts. The machines are neither geniuses nor idiots. No one even slightly acquainted with the nature of their circuits can endow them with mysterious abilities. No one familiar with some of their present limitations, or with the powers of the brain, can claim that they exhibit advanced human intelligence. On the other hand, it is a mistake to dismiss them as nothing but machines, an attitude which one investigator has called "nothing-buttery thinking."

Their speed is so much greater than ours that it amounts to a difference in quality, almost to the creation of a new mental trait. Even blind trial and error can be a potent process if it is fast enough to permit the solution of problems which we could not hope to tackle otherwise—which is exactly what is happening. Furthermore, although it is generally true that computers do what they are told to do, that is not quite the whole truth. For example, in writing a program you may tell a machine to repeat a certain set of arithmetic operations or orders over and over again until it arrives at a number greater or smaller than a certain value. But you do not tell it how many times to repeat the steps, because you do not know yourself. In other words, you cannot predict every step that the machine will carry out, and in that sense, at least, it does something more than you tell it to do. Also a machine can and does change its instructions from time to time, which definitely takes it out of the blind-follower category.

But above all it is important to remember that doing arithmetic, solving mathematical equations by sheer bulldozing power, is not the most significant of the machines' accomplishments. Computers are thinking aids of enormous potentialities. Merely having them around is enough to change the way we think, to force investigators in all fields to think through their problems along new lines. We are at the beginning of a trend that is certain to bring machines which not only learn, but which will accelerate the rate at which we ourselves learn. The revolution to come is difficult to appreciate fully. We only know that science, government, and industry will change swiftly and radically in the years ahead.

Computers are too important to overrate or underrate. There is no real point in sensationalizing or exaggerating activities which are striking enough without embellishment. There is no point in belittling either. It is hardly an insult to existing computers that they fall considerably short of the human brain and are not creative. The difference simply emphasizes with new force the complexity and capabilities of the nervous system, and challenges us to study it as well as our machines more deeply. The more we learn about computers, the better we shall understand and appreciate the nature of thought—and the better we shall use our brains.

CHAPTER 5

THE SEARCH FOR PATTERNS

O NE OF THE FAITHS which has guided science, as it has guided religion and art, is what Einstein called "the ever-firm belief in the harmony of our world." In ancient times men were concerned chiefly with such regularities as the motions of tides, and of the moon, planets, and stars, and the coming and going of seasons. The regularities which command our attention today are less obvious and do not always thrust themselves upon us without intensive study. We seek them out, and the search becomes more and more complex as we learn more and more. It requires, among other things, the analysis of much raw data which may contain evidence of cycles, repetitions, and other patterns and may confirm current hypotheses or lead to new ones.

Electronic computers can do this sort of work. The speed which makes it possible to solve equations too difficult for mathematicians to solve in a reasonable time may also be exploited to analyze information which might otherwise remain unanalyzed. In fact, in many cases investigators would not even bother to gather the information if they did not know beforehand that machines would be available to help them make sense of it. This is where the vicious-circle process comes in. As if life were not complicated enough, we are continually making things more complicated for ourselves. We are not satisfied with using computers only to analyze the kind of data we have been obtaining for years. We go after additional data, in an effort to answer questions that would never have been asked a decade ago.

Take an example which has nothing to do with laboratory research, a national census. In the good old days a census was a relatively simple counting of heads. The 1960 census would hardly fit that description. It asked many more questions than were included in the previous census, and demanded the filling out of elaborate forms by millions of Americans. The forms called for facts about everything from age and sex and occupation and income to employment histories, previous living places, and whether a particular home had an outhouse or a built-in lavatory.

Computers did the main share of sorting and classifying the information on individual forms, and breaking it down into numerous statistical categories. For example, a $2,400,000 Univac at the University of North Carolina worked sixteen hours a day adding numbers—and sorting many types of information contained in the raw census data. Imagine a long series of nine-digit binary expressions such as 100110101, 001110011, 101110111. The expressions can be considered as combinations of three three-digit numbers, and in each expression the middle triplet is 110. This middle-position triplet may be a code for "earns less than $5,000 a year" or "families of five persons or more" or some other category.

Actual operations, of course, involve longer and far more elaborately coded expressions. But the aim is always to recognize meaningful sequences in the codes, to compare and classify information in a thousand and one ways. Computers were also available for the 1950 census. But the improved models of 1960 completed their jobs twelve to eighteen months earlier than would have been possible by previous methods. The statistics they compiled concerned such matters as birth and business trends, changes in family composition, the movements of populations, and employment cycles. An army of other machines performs similar duties in processing data for industrial and military organizations. In many cases they are extracting significant patterns out of masses of unanalyzed information.

Computers may also help bring order out of chaos in organizing large conventions, say, a gathering of scientists. Such conventions tend to confirm the notion that the greater the number of people attending a meeting or conference, the greater the confusion and the less gotten done. Investigators are all too familiar with the problem of trying to be in two places at once, of listening and contributing to one discussion and rushing off to another which may be located several blocks or even several miles away.

Things were somewhat more orderly at a convention of the Federation of American Societies for Experimental Biology held in Chicago more than a year ago. The convention lasted five days and included 250 separate meetings at which nearly 2,400 technical papers were read. As part of their advance planning the organizers of the convention sent questionnaires to more than 3,000 scientists asking them to list the five papers they wanted most to hear and to indicate the order of their preference. This information was conveyed to a computer together with facts about the sizes and locations of rooms available. The machine typed out a master program for the convention, a program in which schedule conflicts were at a minimum. (Significantly, the only difficulty involved the human element. Some investigators failed to specify their interests precisely enough for the computer.)

A closely related problem was handled at the M.I.T.

Computation Center. It concerned a public school which has 3,300 students and offers 225 different courses. A computer prepared a schedule accounting for all students in every one of the school's 1,000 daily classroom periods. The machine arranged things so that each student had a well-balanced set of courses and ample time to go from one class to the next, a factor which is becoming more and more important in large schools with tight schedules. In such applications computers may analyze a large number of different schedules before finding the one which is most appropriate under the given circumstances.

Pattern-seeking often means trying various combinations of data to see which provide the best fits. What sets of aptitudes and personality traits are most characteristic of unusually gifted children? What factors determine our preferences in buying food, clothing, homes, and so on? What can we deduce about changes in ancient communities from changing designs in excavated pottery and other relics? To answer such questions it is necessary to find which of several theories match observed facts, and in many cases computers may do the matching for us, or at least furnish promising clues.

The search for patterns becomes especially intriguing when the object of the game is to conceal rather than convey information. We do not know who devised the first secret cipher. But human nature being what it is, we can assume that the art of deliberately making things difficult to read arose not long after writing was invented five or six thousand years ago. Our earliest records of the art go back to the Greeks, and since then ciphering and deciphering have evolved to such an advanced stage that cryptanalysts rely increasingly on electronic computers.

The most common method of making ciphers is known as double substitution. A famous system of this sort was developed during the sixteenth century by a French dip-

lomat, Blaise de Vigenère, and is somewhat easier to apply than to describe. Suppose you want to send the following message: THE ATTACK WILL START AT
THREE. You and the receiver agree beforehand on a
key word, say, SWIM. Also, you both use the equivalent
of a special slide rule with the twenty-six letters of the
alphabet on the fixed part and a repeating alphabet on
the sliding part. As your first step you move the slide so
that its S, the first letter of your key word, falls under the
A of the fixed alphabet:

ABCDE FGHI JKLMNOPQRSTU VWXYZ

....PQRSTUVWXYZABCDEFGHI JKLMNO PQRSTU....

Having set the slide, you then go to the upper line and
locate T, the first letter of your message. Beneath it, on
the lower line or sliding part, you find L, which becomes
the first letter of your cipher.

Getting the second letter of the cipher calls for a sim-
lar procedure. This time you shift the slide to the left
so that its W (the second letter of the key word) comes
under the A of the fixed alphabet, and find out that H
(the second letter of your message) will be enciphered by
D. And so on and on until the message is completed. You
shift the slide right or left at each step, repeatedly using
the sequence of four letters in the key word. Unless I have
slipped up somewhere, the fully enciphered message should
look something like this: LDM MLPIOC TQXD OBMJP
IF LDZQW. To confuse things a bit more and conceal
the word groupings, you can write it as a set of five-
letter combinations—LDMML PIOCT QXDOB MJPIF
LDZQW—which is a far cry from THE ATTACK WILL
START AT THREE.

This is an exceedingly simple form of double substitution, too trivial for electronic devices. Given a sufficiently

long message or a sufficient number of messages, crypt-analysts could find the key word and solve the cipher easily. For one thing, they have had long experience with double substitutions. Otherwise the job would take much longer. About three centuries passed before a Prussian officer, going through a long and tedious and systematic process of trial and error, cracked the de Vigenère system.

The trick is to search secret messages for telltale repetitions in letters or groups of letters and to analyze the intervals between repetitions. Notice that the process of enciphering the above message has successfully masked the commonest English letter *E*, which appears in the cipher different each time (as *L*, *Q*, and *W*). But notice, too, that both the *TH*'s, in THE and THREE, happened to come out as *LD*'s. The basic nature of double substitution, and of any other class of ciphers—the basic nature of the alphabet itself—is such that there will always be repetitions and cycles and other periodic clues to give the game away. You cannot hide everything.

But modern ciphers involve patterns arrived at with the aid of sophisticated mathematics, and are so complicated that no amount of human trial-and-error analysis could ever solve them. This is precisely the sort of situation in which computers shine. Properly programmed, they can detect coded combinations of letters just as they do in census or indexing problems and go on from there to subtler comparisons. They can try and try again hundreds of thousands of times a second. Of course, no machine is infallible even though it may make fewer errors than a human being. If a cipher is too complicated, there is always the danger of a "garble," a confused or nonsensical result. During the Battle for Leyte Gulf in World War II, a garbled message caused American naval commanders considerable trouble. On the other hand, the Japanese lost the Battle of Midway because their cipher was too simple. It produced no garbles, but American cryptanalysts solved it quickly.

Computers devise as well as solve ciphers. In fact, present-day cryptanalysis pits machine against machine in an international contest which represents one of the most secret of all military endeavors. You can use a computer to be its own enemy, to test a new cipher which it has itself created—and then instruct it to work out more difficult ciphers if the solution is too easy by its built-in standards.

When it comes to extracting meaningful information from jumbled data, however, the most challenging problems of all are encountered in basic scientific research. In cracking a cipher someone generally is in on the secret, so that the correct solution is known. But you are flying blind in basic research. You are studying aspects of natural phenomena which have never been studied before, blazing new trails, and there is no one to tell you whether your guesses or hypotheses are right or wrong. And no one has ever devised riddles as intricate as those which nature presents to basic investigators.

Imagine a New Year's Eve party, a roomful of persons laughing and throwing confetti and blowing tin horns. Off in a corner two less-festive gentlemen are absorbed in a discussion and speaking at a normal conversational level. (Such things have been known to happen.) Now suppose that you have recorded the party, sound effects and all, on a reel of sound tape—and that you are interested only in the conversation. Your microphone was not located near the two gentlemen, but somewhere in the center of the room and picked up everything. But you want to tune out the noise, and listen in on the two serious speakers.

Many analogous problems must be solved during the course of scientific experiments. About three years ago, for example, a team of eight investigators at M.I.T.'s Lincoln

Lincoln Laboratory radar installation used to transmit radar signals to Venus—and to pick up signals or echoes bouncing off the planet. The TX-2 computer analyzed data provided by this equipment.

Laboratory used a high-power dish-shaped radar transmitter to bounce signals off Venus. They sent a series of several thousand pulses out into space, toward the planet. The sending period lasted about five minutes, the round-trip time required for a signal traveling at the speed of light to reach Venus and bounce off and return to earth. So the last pulse left the transmitter just before the first pulse was due back. Then the transmitter was shut off, and the radar set's receiver "listened" for echoes. The echoes were recorded on a reel of magnetic tape.

This is where the problem arises. If you had dream reception, if the tape recorded only echoes from Venus, you could run it on an ordinary sound recorder and hear a series of sharp beeps representing the desired signals. But this tape, like the hypothetical tape of our New Year's Eve party, picked up everything—static from remote radio stars and other emitters in outer space, static arising in the electronic circuits of the radar set itself, perhaps a burst or two from nearby electrical equipment. In other words, weak signals were buried in a hubbub of noise.

The Lincoln Laboratory research group fed the tape into an electronic computer to separate signals from noise. Signals have certain identifying characteristics. Returning to the New Year's Eve party, the conversation took place at a steady sound level, while the laughter and horn-blowing came in bursts of varying intensity. There was a similar difference between the Venus echoes and the interfering noise, and the computer distinguished between them by analyzing its mixed input and finding a consistent pattern that could only have been caused by the reflected radar signals. Stanford University scientists used the same sort of approach in bouncing radar signals off the sun. Such work is of importance in astronomy and missile-tracking because by measuring echo times you can calculate the distances of objects with high precision. Radar and other methods have reached a point where we can soon expect to know the distance of Venus to an accuracy of about one-thousandth of one per cent.

Brain investigators are also interested in distinguishing signals from noise, and have also used computers to help them do it. The cells of the brain produce electrical signals, although not the long-distance kind. They do not normally leave the skull, but they can be recorded by brain-wave or EEG devices. The signals may indicate the presence of disease; they may be SOS signals. But it is often impossible to detect such signals by examining the inked lines of EEG charts, for the characteristic patterns may be lost in the "noise" of ceaseless cerebral activity.

So instead of telltale signatures on the charts you see a hash of irregular ripples. Among those working on this problem is Dr. Mary A. B. Brazier, formerly of the Massachusetts General Hospital, who, cooperating with M.I.T. scientists, turned to the machine in Room 26-248, the TX-0 computer.

One of her patients was a man suffering from loss of vision due to a cerebral stroke involving damage to blood vessels in the brain. His EEG chart was not particularly informative, showing only a jumble of wavy lines. The chart was converted into magnetic-tape form, and the TX-0 computer, in effect, discarded the hash and presented a record of the pure signals. The signals indicated brain-wave disturbances on both sides of the patient's brain. Subsequent computer analysis revealed that his loss of vision was the result of damage on the left side of the brain. Notice how closely this experiment resembles the Venus radar experiment. In both cases, the machine is used to isolate signals masked by the noise of other activity, to pick up one meaningful "voice" in a noisy crowd.

Another major problem is the unfortunate fact that in many experiments most of the material recorded is meaningful but utterly uninteresting. It is something like visiting friends just back from a trip abroad—with a voluminous collection of photographs which they would like you to see. Some of the photographs are fine, showing new or unusual or even exciting faces and scenery. But the rest, and that often means the great majority, might just as well have been taken in your backyard for all they reveal. If your friends would let you separate the interesting from the dull snapshots, all would be well. That rarely happens, though.

Compare this situation with that frequently found at research centers. We have already mentioned what is going on at the University of California's Radiation Laboratory, where automatic cameras take 10,000 pictures a day of the trails of moving atomic particles. As science steps up its studies of the nucleus and the basic properties of matter, there are going to be more and more records of this sort. We can expect some million or more photographs every year from a dozen or so devices besides the one in California.

Such work requires multimillion-dollar atom-smashing machines to create on earth events which occur inside stars and among turbulent gas clouds in galactic space. The photographs which record the events are full of patterns. The lines on them resemble the markings left on ice after an Olympic figure skater has finished a performance, or, better yet, the forms of an abstract painting. There are straight lines, intersecting curves, triangles, full circles and broken arcs, spirals. There is no conventional noise problem here. Investigators can read the patterns the way composers read notes. But they are looking for new "music," signs of rare or hitherto unobserved events which may serve as the basis for new physical laws—and most of the photographs represent often-seen events of no special interest.

The job of poring over thousands or tens of thousands of photographs to find one significant record is tedious and time-consuming. But someone or something has to do it, and be able at least to weed out the uninteresting records and select those which are extraordinary or on the borderline. Considerable research is being conducted to find improved methods of shifting the burden from men to computers. The first step, transforming visual material into electrical signals, can be done in various ways. For example, you can put a photograph on a so-called "facsimile transmitter" which in effect divides the picture into a large number of tiny squares and scans the whole surface square by square.

The scanning of a single square by the transmitter pro-

duces a single voltage. The value of that voltage represents the intensity of light at that part of the photograph.
After the entire photograph has been scanned, the result
may be a series of more than 150,000 voltages each of
which has a specific position in the series. In other words,
the photograph becomes a sequence of voltages. The information can be fed directly into a computer where the
voltages are transformed into a series of binary numbers
with different values arranged in a definite order. You end
up with a binary-digit, or bit, version of the photograph.

This was actually done with the TX-2 computer, a more
recent model in the series of experimental machines which
started with the TX-o. The program prepared for the job
consisted of about a hundred instructions specifying methods of reorganizing the data in a more compact and economical way. The TX-2 completed about a quarter of a
million operations in less than 2½ seconds, and produced
a special punched paper tape of atom-trail photographs.
It was, in effect, serving another machine. The tape was
prepared in a form which could be "understood" by the
ILLIAC computer at the University of Illinois, one of the
places where investigators are developing new methods of
sorting pictures electronically.

The ultimate aim of the research is to put many thousands of photographs on reels of magnetic tape and let
computers do the weeding out. The machines would know
that certain patterns of binary digits represent photographs
of uninteresting events and that all other patterns represent events which may reveal new facts. Working at high
speeds, they would evaluate pictures as fast as (or faster
than) the automatic cameras can take them. Moreover,
they would present the significant pictures on television
screens for visual inspection and perhaps go further, analyzing and interpreting the information.

Such work is not only important to physicists. Physicians have similar problems in the drive to prevent cancer. As part of routine medical checkups and mass examinations, they collect cell samples from the tissues of many people and fix the tissues on glass slides for study under the microscope. By noting the size and density and detailed appearance of cells on the slides, trained observers can distinguish normal tissue from tissue which may become cancerous or shows early signs of the disease. Again, the great majority of slides are negative. The rare positive or suspicious slides serve as the basis for more intensive examination and treatment if necessary.

Medical investigators of the United States Public Health Service have already built a computer which can take over much of this work. Called the cytoanalyzer, it is equipped with the usual scanning device and can examine a cell sample in less than a two hundredth of a second. It demonstrated its possibilities a number of years ago in a mass survey of some hundred thousand citizens of Memphis, Tennessee, and has been further developed since then. The important thing, of course, is that the cytoanalyzer should err on the safe side, not rating as normal cells that are actually abnormal or suspicious-looking, and it does that effectively. The final diagnosis is always made by specialists.

We will hear a great deal more about computers in medicine during the years ahead. Two trends, rising populations and efforts to provide better care for more people, are responsible for a rapid increase in all sorts of medical observation. Add to that the wider use of standard and new devices designed to gather more types of data faster than ever before, and you have a situation that demands the stepped-up application of computing techniques. Brainwave studies are not the only projects in which information is accumulating so swiftly that we do not have time to analyze all of it completely.

The Chicago Heart Association has completed a survey
of about thirty thousand public-school pupils. The survey
confirmed what other studies have found. For one thing,
many children—perhaps as many as 2 out of every 1,000
—are suffering from rheumatic fever and other heart ail-
ments which have not been diagnosed. Also, a significant
number of children known to have heart conditions are
not being allowed to participate in dances, certain sports,
and other activities although they could participate without affecting their health. In making the survey Association workers used "electronic stethoscopes," small microphones placed against the chest, to examine 250 to 300
children a day. The sounds were picked up by an automatic tape-recording unit, and physicians listened to each
child's record later in their offices.

This system may be satisfactory when a survey involves
a single test conducted on a relatively small number of
individuals. But it will not be long before large-scale examinations will involve millions of children and adults and
a whole battery of tests. And many new tests and testing
devices are already developed and ready for use. A recent
list includes automatic high-speed blood-cell counters, electronic pulse-takers and thermometers, and a "radio pill"
—a miniature radio transmitter which can be swallowed
and broadcasts details about conditions inside the body.

New and increased information will help the doctor detect the often-subtle combinations of symptoms and measurements required to diagnose disease. He can then recom-
mend the best treatments known to modern medicine. But
first of all he needs the facts—and patients cannot be
treated unless they are examined. One medical authority
has estimated that if what we already know were applied
universally, the average life-span could be increased to a
hundred years or more. It will take a great deal more than
computers to bring that about. But they will certainly play

a role in presenting the patterns of information upon which diagnoses may be based.

Another example of electronic analysis may seem comparatively trivial, at first consideration. As football fans are well aware, professional coaches and players spend much of their off-field time developing offensive and defensive strategies for forthcoming games. Less widely known is the fact that the Chicago Bears, for one, have consulted a computer to help them analyze bookfuls of statistics involving long series of hundreds of their opponents' plays. The machine was instructed to look for trends in the use of offensive plays—what plays opposing teams would tend to call for within their own 10- or 20-yard line, at a number of positions deep in Bear territory, near the end of the game, against different defenses, under various weather conditions, and so on.

One day, according to a recent report, the Bears' coaches were studying machine-analyzed statistics and motion pictures, and found "a pattern in the thinking" of Johnny Unitas, star quarterback of the Baltimore Colts. In certain specific situations he always called for a pass play which sent four potential receivers downfield and left only one man, a halfback, to block out opposing defenders while he got set for the pass. This knowledge was put to use during a game several years ago. Whenever such a situation arose, the Bears sent two oversized defensive ends crashing in on the weakly protected passer. By the time Unitas figured out what was happening, and it is a credit to him that he managed to during the game, most of the contest was over. He had completed only three passes and had three passes intercepted. (The report did not state which team finally won.)

What applies to football may also apply to more serious and costly games. Computers may be useful wherever there are complex competitive situations in which human fallibility plays a significant role. In business and war, for example, our habits as individuals are potential weaknesses as well as strengths. They represent the regularity and predictability and order in our lives. But they may also get us into trouble if we are unconscious of them and cannot alter them to meet altering circumstances. The same thing goes for the collective habits known as established policies, for anything that might offer opportunities to those who would defeat or outsell or replace us.

Call them what you will—plays, habits, trends, customs, mores, traditions—they are all patterns of human behavior. Computers have no ingrained memories, no vested interests, and no axes to grind. So they can often provide us with facts necessary for insights into the effectiveness of our patterns and various alternatives, insights more objective perhaps than those we might achieve without electronic aid. It has been said that every war is lost by leaders who are still fighting the preceding war, and there is undoubtedly a germ of truth in this, although unequal forces and research facilities may also determine the outcome. In any case, the Department of Defense has many computers seeking and analyzing patterns in practice military maneuvers and mock battles.

To take a single detailed instance, suppose an enemy plane is being intercepted by defending jet fighters. What specifically is the pilot likely to do in his efforts to get away? Will he dive sharply or climb, turn to the right or left, fly a curving or straight course? The problem is not to predict the behavior of any particular pilot, but the behavior of a "statistical" pilot. Computers can analyze the actions of many thousands of pilots in many different situations, and calculate the most probable among all attempted escape tactics. The actions of men in tanks or submarines or missile-guiding ground stations may be similarly studied.

Finally, we come to research involving the operation of computer systems themselves. Important studies are being conducted to improve sensing, or input, devices. These devices are designed specifically to recognize patterns of holes or magnetic spots on reels of tape, but it is only a matter of time before they are surpassed in many applications. After all, we developed such codes because of the limitations of machines currently in widespread use. The fact that they cannot read printed material directly puts the burden on us to translate our instructions into computer language. Sooner or later we will shift a large part of the burden to them.

But the problem of developing electronic readers is far from simple. Some time ago visitors to the Lincoln Laboratory provided material for continuing experiments in pattern recognition. They were asked to print their names and addresses in a series of quarter-inch squares, one character to a square. A study of the samples showed that even when we print, our writing may vary considerably. Laboratory workers trying to identify individual characters, letters and numbers presented randomly and one at a time, failed in about three out of every hundred cases. Since we cannot afford such an error rate in computing problems, it is clear right from the start that electronic readers will have to be superior to human readers.

The first step is not particularly difficult. You can present a letter on a grid, a screen of tiny squares, and use photoelectric cells to do the scanning. The squares that include part of the letter will be black and can be coded as binary 1's; the empty squares are 0's. Thus, the letter —like an atom-trail photograph—is represented by a series of binary digits. Now the trouble begins. To tell one letter from another, a machine must recognize unique patterns in its binary codes. In effect, it must do exactly what we do unconsciously and automatically as we read. There is no single pattern that positively distinguishes one hand-written letter from all the rest. *M* has two lines which converge to a point in the middle; so do *X* and *Y*. It has two parallel vertical lines, and so do *H* and *N*. When we read, we detect groups of patterns and compare them. A machine must do the same thing.

Preliminary experiments at M.I.T. indicate what this means. One report, "The Recognition of Sloppy, Hand-Printed Characters," describes a recent Lincoln Laboratory research project. The investigator, Worthie Doyle, confined himself to the task of programming a computer to identify only ten selected letters: *A, E, I, L, M, N, O, R, S, T.* Yet even this task required the analysis of twenty-eight different features, the search for twenty-eight different possible types of patterns. Does the letter have an open space or "concavity" above or below or at the sides? Does it have one or more vertical or horizontal lines, or a crossbar? What is the largest number of intersections that can be produced by drawing a horizontal line through the letter? A vertical line?

The computer read hundreds of versions of the ten selected letters as hand-printed by visitors to the laboratory. It subjected them to the entire battery of twenty-eight tests and calculated probabilities for each test. For example, take the test which involves drawing a horizontal line through a letter. The machine examined 330 "sloppy" letters by this test and found that if the letter is intersected at a maximum of three points, the odds are as follows: better than one in three that it is an *N*, one in four that it is an *M*, about one in fifteen for an *E*, and so on. (Of course, the machine figured the odds more precisely, to three decimal places.) The computer arranged the results of all the tests on all the letters in what amounts to a set of probability tables.

Now, on the basis of this built-in experience, it was

ready to read new samples. Confronted with one of the ten letters, a hand-printed version it had never seen before, it proceeded to apply the tests and consult the tables and figure the odds. For each possible letter it calculated total scores, and the letter with the highest score "won" —that is, the machine identified the letter by typing it out or displaying it on a television-type screen. Tests showed that the computer analysis produced identifications somewhat more accurate than human readers, which is better than 97 per cent and represents an appreciable accomplishment, particularly considering the complexity of the problem.

As we have seen, however, the results are still limited. Not only is the machine restricted to recognizing ten letters out of the whole alphabet, but it must be fed each letter one at a time and is still helpless when confronted by anything as formidable as a simple word. Yet investigators are generally optimistic about developments for the not-too-distant future. Although the sloppy-handwriting problem is by no means solved, electronic devices are already available which can read less variable material, such as the letters printed by typewriters and other machines.

Meanwhile there is a great deal of work to be done on a much more difficult problem, the recognition of speech. Existing computers have spent many hundreds of hours seeking acoustic patterns which future machines could use to identify spoken words received through microphones. Even assuming this might be possible, how could we program a computer so that it would not be fooled by "puns" —so that it could distinguish "bow" from "bough," or "two" from "too" and "to"? We are still a long way from the ultimate in office dictating machines, a voice-writer which listens to your words and types them out as rapidly as you speak.

Progress is coming slowly, but remember what we are

up against. Although recognizing a letter may not seem like a striking feat, it calls for a high order of analytic ability. You can identify a given letter whether it is large or small, capitalized, italicized, upside down, or even in mirror-image form. It may be printed in any one of a large number of different types. Yet you automatically discard every unimportant difference and come up with the basic similarity—the signs that identify the letter once and for all. You rid the image of all but its essential pattern.

You are guided not only by the particular letter before you at the time, but also by your memories of previous viewings—by an abstract idea of the letter. The same process is at work when we recognize a familiar face, a cry for help, a tune played in swing or Dixieland style, a courteous gesture. So machines that recognize and respond meaningfully to written or spoken information would be exhibiting one of the most powerful features of mental activity. They would be selecting patterns in the light of past experience, forming abstractions. Such machines do not exist yet. But no one familiar with current computer research doubts that they will come eventually.

CHAPTER 6

VARIETIES OF MODELS

A NUMBER OF YEARS AGO persons visiting the Army's Waterways Experiment Station in Clinton, Mississippi, would have seen a most unusual type of "landscape gardening." Engineers were at work in an open field building something which reminded you of the toy scenery designed for children's electric trains, only on a more extensive scale. Instead of tracks there were meandering concrete runways to represent rivers, little dams and spillways and reservoirs, bridges, and so on. Plans called for careful grading of the land, including miniature mountains up to 50 feet in height and valleys shaped according to geographical contours.

It was all part of one of the most elaborate systems of its kind ever conceived—a model of the entire Mississippi watershed stretching east to west from New York to the Continental Divide, from the Appalachians to the Rockies, and north to south from Canada to the Gulf of Mexico. Some 1,244,000 square miles of the United States were to be included in about 200 acres of rolling land, eight miles of concrete-runway rivers simulating 15,700 miles of actual navigable waterways. Measured quantities of water would flow through pipes into the runways to produce normal or flood conditions. Thus, about a cubic foot a second flowing past the model site of Vicksburg would represent more than 2 million cubic feet a second, the amount that actually flowed past the city in the disastrous 1937 flood. The time scale was adjusted so that 5½ minutes represented twenty-four hours of real time.

This system, designed for flood-control studies, is an example of a general method used in laboratories throughout the world, the making of models. Precisely machined steel-and-ceramic models of Mercury capsules, the vehicles which will carry the first American astronauts into space, are routinely constructed at the Langley Field Research Center of the National Space and Aeronautics Administration in Virginia. Protective nose devices for blunt projectiles with fins, disks shaped like flying saucers, thin triangular "flying wings," and other experimental models are placed in special shock tunnels which simulate conditions encountered when a returning spaceship traveling 5 to 6 miles a second re-enters the earth's atmosphere. (Surface temperatures of the devices may rise nearly as high as temperatures at the sun's surface, about 12,000 degrees Fahrenheit.)

Wind tunnels test miniature airplanes and airplane parts, rockets, helicopters, bridges, skyscrapers. Toylike ocean liners and warships and submarines are towed in tanks and basins. In these and many other cases the engineer is looking for flaws which can be corrected before production gets under way. Models may be scaled up as well as down. Most of us have seen intricate lattice-like structures which look something like Erector-set productions and represent the arrangements of atoms in chemical compounds. Such structures are billions of times bigger than the actual molecules.

But there is also a different type of model-making, the creation of intangible "invisible" models. In this approach the investigator does not use solid materials and tools to shape them. He does not have to build elaborate testing apparatus. He works entirely with ideas, abstractions which may be expressed in words or mathematical symbols. The statement "consider a star with twice the mass of the sun contracting under the influence of its internal gravitational field" outlines the design of a model just as effectively as a rough blueprint. The difference is that we proceed to build such models in our heads. We express our ideas and observed data in symbols more precise than the machined forms of actual objects. Some of the nonlinear equations discussed in a previous chapter may be regarded as condensed statements written in mathematical language and representing models which we conceive of but do not build.

Take the equation $\ddot{x} + (a\dot{x} + b\dot{x}^2 + cx) = 0$. This is the equation for the angle of rolling, x, of a ship in still water. Another equation, $x_{ab} = w + w'(x + y) + (x + z)(s + w' + z)(z' + y + s'v)$, represents the design characteristics of a simple electrical circuit. Solving equations may amount to the same thing as building a model and studying its behavior under carefully controlled experimental conditions, or observing the course of actual events. Abstract ideas are necessary but not sufficient. We also need the right kind of measurements to specify as exactly as possible the dimensions and operations of our models. Given that information, we can conceive of an enormous variety of models—and run the most complicated on electronic computers.

This opens up an entirely new area. The machines are systems which can simulate things that happen or may happen in real life. The information that flows through their circuits in the form of electrical pulses may be so organized that, within the limits of our abilities to specify reality, a computer in effect conducts certain kinds of experiments. It can reproduce events which occurred in times past, or create events which have not yet occurred or may never occur. It can help us re-explore the past and investigate possible futures. In this sense, the computer is the closest thing to a time machine that man has yet invented.

As our first example, consider the problem of flood control and the landscape-gardening model in Mississippi. One thing you want to know about the model (and any model) is how well it represents actual phenomena, and reproducing a former flood is a good way of checking up. First you might adjust pipe valves so that normal amounts of water flow along concrete runways representing the Mississippi River and three of its major tributaries—the Arkansas, Red, and Tennessee Rivers. Then you go back to the records, find out how much water velocities and depths increased in each of the tributaries during a past flood season, and increase the corresponding quantities in the runways. Finally, you measure changes in depth and flow rates in the largest runway, the one representing the Mississippi River. If the changes correspond to what actually happened, you may be confident in the design of your model.

The same thing can be done using a computer. In this case the model is a theoretical system, perhaps a set of equations describing the behavior of rivers. The details of the model can be written out as a program of instructions. Instead of building runways, you can also write out the depths, widths, and lengths of various rivers—as well as the specific effects of normal and flood conditions. All this information and more may be put on punch cards or magnetic tape and stored in a magnetic-core memory. Then you push a button and the computer will re-create the flood electronically.

Experiments of this sort have been tried at a number of research centers, including the Institute of Mathematical Sciences of New York University. A few years ago J. J.

Stoker and his associates had developed a mathematical river-flow model and wanted to check its validity. So they selected the Ohio River floods of 1945, concentrating on events involving the river and its tributaries along the 375-mile stretch from Wheeling, West Virginia, to Cincinnati. A computer took two hours to figure out what would happen, according to the model, in two real-time weeks of flooding. It calculated the flood crest of the Ohio River to an accuracy of better than an inch and a half, a good indication of how closely the mathematical model represents actuality.

So much for historical studies, the rerunning of past floods. To explore possible futures, investigators can assume various rainfalls affecting any tributary or combination of tributaries and let computers work out the details of hypothetical floods. They specify how much and how fast and where river levels will rise. More than that, they can help us develop tactics to prevent or minimize floods yet to come. Building dams is only part of the flood-control problem. A river system like that in the Mississippi watershed may have hundreds of dams, and control will not be effective unless the dams are operated in a coordinated way.

Heavy spring rains may fill a reservoir along the Muskingum River in southeastern Ohio. That prevents local flooding. But the reservoir has to be unloaded before more rains send torrents pouring over dam tops, and engineers must release waters slowly enough to swell but not flood the river. People living along the Muskingum may be safe, but what about those along the Ohio—which picks up water from the Muskingum and from many other rivers with reservoir systems of their own? And how can you control waters along the Ohio and Tennessee Rivers to avoid flooding the Mississippi? Such operations require elaborate and rapid timing throughout networks of dams, and that is a suitable job for the computer. It can simulate not only future floods, but also the countermeasures that will save lives and property.

The control of air traffic is another problem whose solution calls for "computer" type models. Public attention was focused on this problem about a year ago when the collision of two planes over Brooklyn killed 134 persons in the worst disaster of aviation history. Bumper-to-bumper driving and full-up parking lots have become a familiar part of the American scene, but it still takes a catastrophe to make us realize that, even though planes have an extra dimension to move around in, air traffic is beginning to cause at least as much trouble as ground traffic. Although accidents are rare, safety may mean that your plane has to circle around until a landing strip is clear or wait in line for its turn to take off.

And one thing is sure: things are not going to become less complicated. Take one of the world's busiest air terminals, New York International Airport in Long Island. The odds are that at any moment on a clear midmorning hour there will be 100 to 150 planes over its "target area" (a circle with the Airport at the center and a fifty-mile radius). Judging by expected increases in air traffic, experts estimate that within fifteen years the same space will contain some 350 planes. Engineers, pilots, airline executives, and government authorities have ideas about what might be done to speed up present-day services and allow for future expansion. Computers are putting some of their ideas to the test.

Here again it is a matter of proper programming. You write out a descriptive model of a certain volume of air space which contains, say, a hundred planes located at specified positions. Each plane has its speed, altitude, and direction. Some are landing at airports whose dimensions must be specified; others are entering the air space from remote points; still others are taking off. A set of instructions tells the machine how to provide a second-by-second analysis of this complex situation. Furthermore, it is a relatively easy job to produce all sorts of hypothetical situations by increasing the number of planes, "building" new or larger airports, altering flight plans, and making many other changes on the model.

One of the projects sponsored by the Federal Aviation Agency was such a model representing two hours of heavy traffic over the New York metropolitan area. A computer analyzed a series of different situations, in each case taking about six minutes to run through two hours of traffic events. The study showed, among other things, that waiting to land accounted for three-quarters of the delay time for all flights, a conclusion which confirmed a prevailing suspicion. Engineers tried varying many factors, and the one which made the greatest difference was doubling the landing capacity of every airport in the model area. This change reduced delay times by 60 per cent. Unfortunately it is more difficult to add landing strips to a real airport, but at least computers help indicate the sort of changes which will produce important results.

Incidentally, analogous problems occur in industry. Take a steel plant with a certain number of rolling mills and fabricating machines. The equipment can turn out a certain amount of finished steel every hour. But there is a backlog of orders, each requiring different times on different machines, and the main job of executives and foremen is to schedule the available time of every machine as efficiently as possible. Offhand you might not think of this as a traffic problem, but you can consider every order as as plane looking for a place to land and the machines as the rough equivalent of an airport with a specified capacity.

IBM mathematicians have worked out a program to handle such situations. Known as the "JSS (job shop simulator) program," it consists of a set of about nine thousand general instructions for making an almost unlimited number of models. The instructions are coded on a deck of some 375 punch cards, and copies of the decks are available to industry. Given a deck, engineers can describe any scheduling problem at their plant and feed the details into an IBM computer. Then the cards tell the machine what to do, and the machine in turn tells the engineers whether it would be better to buy new machines or give certain types of orders top priority or take some alternative course. To date, General Electric, U.S. Steel, and eighty other major American corporations have used the master JSS program.

Other programs deal with an entirely different class of models, models conceived during the course of basic research and representing theories in action. Investigators require electronic help in developing new concepts about the nature of the universe. We have come a long way from ancient notions about the fixed and eternal stars. Research reveals that active stars, including our sun, are vast gas furnaces which burn nuclear fuels and continuously build fresh supplies of the chemical elements out of atomic particles. When their fuels become exhausted, they may sputter out slowly like fading embers or explode with the force of millions of hydrogen bombs. They are dying all the time, and stellar infants are being born. At the present stage in the history of the Milky Way galaxy birth rates exceed death rates. On the average, one star shrinks into a dwarf or dying state and three to four new stars come into being every year.

Astronomers may never be able to create a miniature newborn star in the laboratory and watch it pass through youth, middle age, and senility. But a general-purpose computer can simulate stars as well as floods or traffic conditions. In this case you specify the mass of the model star, the amounts of nuclear fuels (hydrogen and helium) at its interior, and other relevant information based on telescopic observations. Then the star evolves in the computer, as it were. It is as if you had a time-lapse motion picture of the event, with each frame representing a hundred thousand years—and billions of years of evolution taking place in a matter of hours.

A computer study at the California Institute of Technology indicates that a certain star in the Milky Way is 16 billion years old. If other studies yield similar findings, we may have to revise astronomical methods of dating cosmic events. Apparently there is nothing wrong with the stellar model or with the data upon which the machine's calculations were based. Yet the age of the expanding universe is believed to be about 10 billion years, considerably less than the age of one of its stars, and some theories will have to be readjusted before the contradiction is ironed out.

Recently astronomers borrowed time from a high-speed computer at the Atomic Energy Research Establishment in Harwell, England. They used it as a kind of solar-system model to explore the implications of evidence that comets vanish at a high rate, either by escaping from the solar system or disintegrating within it. In effect the scientists filled the hypothetical skies of the model with hypothetical comets, some 1,500,000 of them, or about as many as would appear in half a million years or so of real time. Each comet followed a statistical course determined by the probabilities that the sun and planets would deflect its course. The machine indicated that during a period of 200 million years ninety-nine out of every hundred comets disappear—and threw a question back at its programmers. Since the solar system is billions of years old, why hasn't our supply of comets dwindled away long ago? (According to one theory, new comets are being created from matter at the outermost regions of the solar system.)

This sort of statistical model-making was first used during World War II for secret studies at the Los Alamos Scientific Laboratory. John von Neumann, thinking of gamblers and odds and roulette wheels, gave the method the code name "Monte Carlo," and the name has stuck. It is still being used in secret work as well as in many nonmilitary fields. You can run various kinds of trajectories on computers with the Monte Carlo method—say, the trajectories of neutrons which trigger and maintain nuclear chain reactions. The workings of atomic weapons and power plants depend to an appreciable extent on how effectively the walls of containers reflect or absorb these particles.

But it is purely a matter of chance whether an individual particle escapes or bounces back or is absorbed. The particle may hit some of the atoms in the wall head-on or, more likely, sideswipe them and move off in any one of a number of directions. There are so many possibilities that investigators employ the Monte Carlo statistical approach in studying the hit-and-run tactics of wandering neutrons. They program computers to simulate random zigzagging pathways of enough neutrons to provide a valid sample.

Here is an account of such a study by a Los Alamos scientist, Daniel McCracken: "In one very simple problem on which I assisted, an electronic computer labored for three hours to trace the life histories of 10,000 neutrons through 1,500,000 collisions. I would have had to sit at a desk calculator for some years to accomplish the same result." More advanced problems simulate traffic conditions among far greater numbers of particles and may require days or weeks, even with the aid of the fastest computers in existence. To mention a further Monte Carlo application, biologists have developed programs to study detailed mechanisms in the multiplication of cancer cells.

Among the most complex basic-research models currently being studied are those involving the human brain. The analysis of brain waves, discussed in the preceding chapter, presents many formidable problems. But at least we start with a real brain and some of the raw data generated in it, records of rhythmical electrical activity. The records help us understand the organ producing them. In model experiments you come at things from the opposite direction. There is far less to go on, far less "real" information. You try to start with a hypothetical system which might turn out to work the way the brain works in certain respects. That is, the system might generate raw data comparable to the data generated by an actual brain (although this stage has not yet been reached).

A representative study is that of Belmont Farley and Wesley Clark at the Lincoln Laboratory. One of the systems they described and fed into the TX-2 computer consisted of a network of 1,296 (36 times 36) "neurons," or nerve cells, each cell being connected with from ten to thirty other cells. This might represent part of the cerebral cortex or "outer bark" of the brain, a thin sheet of closely packed cells which is the highest nerve center of all. The network is displayed on the screen of a cathode-ray tube in the form of a square array of spots. When simulated stimuli pass into the network, groups of the spots brighten and produce glowing patterns which represent nervous responses.

The model operates in slow motion. The computer takes less than five seconds to simulate events that would occur in a thousandth of a second in an array of real nerve cells. The characteristics may be varied in many ways. All the cells may have the same thresholds—that is, they all respond to signals above some minimum value—or different thresholds. Furthermore, these values may be changed during an experiment, so that you can observe the results directly in changing patterns on the screen. The patterns, spiral-like forms or expanding ripples of activity or irregular groups of scintillating spots, may indicate how nerve-cell systems are altered as a result of experience.

If you are thinking in terms of "model brains," however, a word of caution is in order. This research has exciting possibilities, and "there are grounds for hope that significant cortical functions can be 'simulated.'" But right now things are at the earliest stages. A network of 1,000 to 2,000 nerve cells ranks rather low on the evolutionary scale. There are many more cells in the brain of an ant or a bee, and the human cortex contains some 10 billion cells. It should also be noted that the individual nerve cells simulated on the model are simplified versions of the basic electricity-producing units in the brain. So deeper insights will have to await the development of more refined models and computer programs.

The use of models will have far-reaching effects in another area. The social sciences have lagged relative to other fields of research, largely because the phenomena with which they deal are far more complex. The physical sciences have reached a new high point in the study and exploitation of the nucleus, while biologists seem to have defined the basic problems whose solution is expected to bring significant advances in the years ahead. But it is easier to be objective about atoms and cells than about people, and the social sciences have a rather rough time trying to get rid of preconceived notions concerning "human nature" and group behavior.

One factor which hints at accelerated progress in the future is described in the 1960 annual report of the National Science Foundation: "The electronic computer promises to enlarge the social scientist's opportunity to manipulate complex systems, and to understand better their systematic properties through constructing models of social and economic processes. Simulation studies are currently being supported on such diverse social processes as settlement and migration, conflict, and public discussion and choice."

We are familiar, of course, with the use of computers in one notable area of "public discussion and choice" (and, to some extent, of "conflict" as well)—presidential elections. Only two hours after the first polls closed in 1952 a computer predicted that Eisenhower would win a landslide victory and figured his electoral total to within four votes. Although no one believed this early answer at the time, people were readier to believe four years later, and in 1956 an accurate prediction was available before the first 300,000 popular votes had been counted.

Electronic analyses were less spectacular during the Kennedy-Nixon election. As Election Night 1960 wore on and viewers in more than 40 million American homes watched figures flashed on glamorous tally boards, it became obvious that few people would be going to sleep with any certainty about who the next president would be. A proportion of viewers had the strong impression that the computers were as confused as the rest of us. But the machines have not yet evolved to the stage where they are capable of confusion. As a matter of fact, they performed quite commendably in a situation which differed markedly from the two previous elections in respect to the religious issue and the extreme closeness of the popular vote.

We should think twice before condemning the machines too harshly. What is the real source of the disappointment we may feel when they fall short of our expectations? Precisely what has been overrated, their capabilities or ours? The machines must be judged innocent. Pointing the finger at them during presidential elections, for example, is a pure and simple case of mistaken identity. You might just as well blame a rock for stubbing your toe, or a car for getting into an accident when the driver tries passing a truck on a curve in a fog. Until we develop machines that learn as efficiently as our current models do sums, they will continue to reflect our own insights and limitations.

In any case, the appearance of computers on Election Night television shows has been amply publicized. We have heard far less about another most important application which affected the planning of a campaign. During the summer of 1960 a 46-page report was completed and included the following excerpts:

> Kennedy has a firm advantage over Nixon in terms of personality. His personality comes over on TV better than Nixon's. The image of Kennedy is that he is friendlier and more congenial than Nixon. This is not a matter of sex-appeal. Men feel Kennedy is friendlier almost two to one . . . while women feel the two candidates are more nearly equal in appeal.

> Kennedy today has lost the bulk of the votes he would lose if the election campaign were to be embittered by the issue of anti-Catholicism. . . . There has already been a serious defection from Kennedy by Protestant voters.

> Negro voters are a danger point for the Kennedy campaign. . . . In 1952 and 1954 Negroes gave the Democrats about three quarters of their votes. In 1956 and 1958 they gave the Democrats only two thirds of their votes. Before the conventions and their clarification of the civil rights issue, they were prepared to give the Democrats a narrow majority in a Kennedy-Nixon battle.

These are some of the points made in one of three reports completed on August 25, 1960. Its title was "Kennedy before Labor Day"; the other two reports were "Nixon before Labor Day" and "Kennedy, Nixon and Foreign Affairs." More than three months previously there had been another report, "Negro Voters in Northern Cities." All the reports were marked STRICTLY CONFIDENTIAL, delivered to Kennedy headquarters, and supported with the aid of $60,000 received from the New York Reform Democrats. They were the work of the Simulmatics Corporation, a group organized by three social scientists—Ithiel de Sola Pool of M.I.T., a political scientist; William McPhee of Columbia University, a sociologist; and Robert Abelson of Yale University, a psychologist.

Their reports were based on a unique model. Raw data for the model came from a library of past polls at Williams College (the polls selected dating back to 1952) and included information on attitudes toward major issues as well as stated voting preferences. Sixty-six national public opinion surveys representing more than 100,000 interviews met the initial specifications. Further analysis produced a list of voter categories: "Eastern seaboard, metropolitan, well-to-do, Protestant, Republican male"; "Southern, rural, poor, Protestant, Democratic female"; "Border state, poor, Negro, Independent male"; and so on. In all, 480 different types of voters were identified.

The next step was to select factors which influenced their decisions during past elections. That led to another list of fifty major issues, such as civil rights, fear of war, foreign aid, attitude toward Nixon, defense preparations, and labor. Then a computer entered the picture, but not yet for model purposes. At this stage its sole job was to organize the information accumulated. Imagine a huge chart, a kind of checkerboard array of 24,000 (480 times 50) squares. Each square includes facts about the attitudes of one of the 480 voter types toward one of the fifty major issues. The computer rearranged the information into such blocks, producing a data book thicker than a New York telephone directory. All the information ended up in coded form on reels of magnetic tape.

These reels represent the first requirement for a unique model. They amount to a complete description of a syn-

thesized population of voters, as if a large number of individuals had been interviewed in one mass survey. Given
the description, the computer could then be programmed
to simulate how people in each one of the 480 categories
would vote if an issue increased or decreased in importance.
This is equivalent to conducting hypothetical interviews
in a hypothetical social situation. For example, the computer indicated that if feeling about the Catholic issue
became more intense, pro-Kennedy percentages nationally
would not drop any more than they already had by August.
At any time the religious issue would make little net difference in the East—while in the rest of the country, in
the South and West and Border states, its impact had
already been fully felt.

Many situations were run on the voting model. The total
machine time required for the entire job came to fifty-seven
hours. The resulting reports included lists of the seven
states most favorable to Kennedy (he won all but one of
them), seventeen "hopeless" states (Kennedy lost all but
one), and a great deal of other information and suggestions.
Asked whether the reports had any effect on the planning
of the Democrats' campaign, Pool replied: "The only thing
a researcher can ask is that his reports be read. We know
the Kennedy brothers read our reports the day they got
them."

The model will be used in future studies. It could simulate the effect on voters of a war in Africa or South America,
a boom or bust stock market, or a sharp change in the unemployment situation. Of course, no model is perfect. This
one and all other existing models in the social sciences
represent the beginnings of a development which is certain
to have an enormous impact on our basic understanding
of human behavior—as well as on the applied art of winning friends and influencing people.

The world of business and industry is also ripe for an

increasing use of models. One of the leading investigators in this field is Jay Forrester of M.I.T., a pioneer in the design of magnetic-core memories and the SAGE air defense system. A number of years ago he moved from his computer laboratory to the Institute's School of Industrial Management, where he is concentrating on techniques which have brought about "a major breakthrough for decision makers." During our last conversation he showed me a record of a representative problem, information printed by the automatic typewriter output unit of an electronic computer. It consisted of a strip of paper about a foot wide and perhaps 15 feet long.

The first part of the record was a complete description of the business under study, a company manufacturing electronic products—its present policies, production rates, inventories, orders and times required to fill orders, sales, prices, and so on. All the data were fed into the machine in exactly three-tenths of a second. The rest of the record represented a "trial run," a model of what would happen to business if customer orders were to increase by a certain amount. The machine entered new orders in the company's books, stepped up factory production to keep pace with diminishing inventories, figured out the cost of extra materials and labor, and simulated the entire activities of the business for a period of 400 weeks.

Then it typed out the results of the market change. Included in the results were series of Y's printed one under the other in various positions on the strip of paper. By drawing a line through the letters, you get curves showing month-by-month business fluctuations. Here is how it works:

The dotted line forms a chart, and this particular record included many such charts indicating changes in everything from production to customer purchases. The entire 400-week simulation required about fourteen minutes of computer time.

In setting up a business model, you use two basic types of equations. So-called "level equations" express such things as inventories, unfilled orders, bank balances, and the number of employees at a given time. The other kind of equation describes rates of change resulting from decisions—consumer decisions to buy products, retailer decisions affecting new orders to the company, and company decisions affecting its production and inventories. Problems can be solved rapidly using the latest commercially available machines. A simple industrial problem involving fifty equations and a 100-week run would take about thirty-seven seconds of computer time; a 2,000-equation economic system operating for ten years might take seven minutes.

Machine time is negligible compared with the time required to study problems and prepare suitable model concepts. (The preparation time may range from two months to two or three years.) But as more and more models are run and experience accumulates, this difficulty will become far less significant. Many problems resemble one another so closely that a single basic model may serve for the whole lot, and investigators will have access to a growing library of punch cards and tapes specifying the structure of important models. Furthermore, as executives become accustomed to new electronic and analytical techniques, they will routinely obtain the sort of information which computers require.

Currently most problems are handled on the basis of experience, rule-of-thumb decision, and intuition. This can often bring about the desired results. But not always. Study shows that a number of companies, for example, mistakenly assumed that rising and falling demands for their products were due to seasonal factors. So they established certain policies which had the effect of actually creating seasonal changes—thus confirming their original errors. In other companies policies designed to prevent fluctuations in the size of labor forces have had just the opposite of the intended effect and aggravated the problem.

Such cases will be less frequent in the future. Professor Forrester has summarized the present state of affairs: " 'Controlled laboratory experiments' on industrial and economic situations are now possible with computers to do the work of mathematical models. . . . Circumstances can be studied that might seldom be encountered in the real world. Daring changes that might seem too risky to try with an actual company can be investigated. The manager, like the engineer, can now have a laboratory in which to learn quickly and at low cost the answers that would seldom be obtainable from trials on real organizations."

A breakthrough has been made, although the full effects are not likely to become evident for a decade or two. But computers will certainly be handling bigger and bigger problems, problems requiring several thousand equations. Professor Forrester and his colleagues, for example, are already working on or planning models of the entire national economy of the United States. Another project is to determine the different possible growth patterns of a newly developing country in Africa or South America. It may not be long before some new government becomes the first in history to base its guiding policies on information provided by scientists and computers working in collaboration.

Accompanying all this work will be a steady improvement in computers and computer systems—and that brings us to a most intriguing type of model. We have already indicated that a computer may help figure out the complex wiring for other computers. But there is a great deal more to the story of how computers are used to build computers. Indeed, this is one of the most dramatic examples of an area in which yesterday's science fiction has become routine practice.

Two general principles hold in developing any model for a computer. First you prepare a description of the model whether it be a flood, a star, a nerve network, a voting population, or an industrial system. Then you write out a description of how you want the model to work. Why not use the same procedure for a model of a computer itself? Assume that engineers are setting out to design a new machine, computer A. This machine does not yet exist as a piece of tangible equipment. It exists only in the world of ideas, in the engineer's mind. It is a mental image, a product of the imagination. But it can be described precisely, and that is sufficient for the purpose at hand.

The trick is to describe the design of computer A, put the description on reels of tape, and feed the information into the memory unit of computer B—a real-life, honest-to-goodness machine. Engineers run regular model tests, operating computer A on or in computer B. And the simulated computer works. It does just what it would do if it had been built. If it has not been properly conceived, if its design has flaws, it will make mistakes as it runs through simulated operations. Then the design is changed in an effort to eliminate the operating errors. If the changes are successful, computer A is ready to be built and will become a reality.

Remington Rand engineers experimented with this procedure in designing the first Larc computer. They started out by preparing a set of drawings, logical blueprints of a sort. The drawings were translated into logical equations which, in turn, were translated into a so-called "signals list" showing the origin and termination of every connection among the logical circuits of the machine. The list amounted to a complete description of the machine's components and 100,000 connections. It was converted into eight reels of tape containing the information coded in the form of more than 80 million binary digits.

Using the appropriate reels, a description of the arithmetic unit of the as-yet-unbuilt Larc was placed in the memory of a real-life Univac computer. Then special programs told Univac to run a model of the unit in operation. Univac proceeded to test the simulated electronic circuits of the arithmetic unit by giving it simulated problems to solve. The unit in effect performed hundreds of thousands of additions, subtractions, multiplications, and divisions—and all the time engineers kept close tabs on its operation and modified its circuitry when necessary. The same types of tests were run on a simulated control unit, which directed the flow of simulated signals in and out of simulated arithmetic, memory, and output units.

On the basis of such work investigators at a number of laboratories are using computers to help build computers. We are reducing the trial-and-error element in design. It is no longer necessary to build actual units or entire machines and correct all design errors by modifying electronic hardware. From now on we shall be learning by a new variety of experience, by creating and testing hypothetical computers so that when it comes to building actual machines, many mistakes will have been caught beforehand. Of course, this is also true in the use of any sort of model. All models save us work in dealing with real situations.

But there is something special about the computer situation, an evolutionary element. Univacs I and II, for example, have been used in designing Univac III—and this development represents a new direction in the history of machinery. The records of all other devices fall into an age-old and thoroughly familiar pattern. We always learn as we go. We recognize that a new automobile or jet engine is more than an improvement on previous engines. It is also a guide to the nature of further improvements. Engineers will study it in operation and go on from there to more advanced engines.

Only in the case of computers, however, can you actually use a machine to do part of the direct work necessary for producing a similar machine which will surpass it. This approach is something like lifting yourself up by your own bootstraps. As computers become faster and hold more in their memories, they become more and more valuable in simulating their successors. In a significant sense, in a sense that has never been true before, we can expect the evolution of computers to be increasingly a self-feeding and self-accelerating process.

CHAPTER 7

ARTIFICIAL INTELLIGENCE

O N OCTOBER 26, 1960, a nationwide television audience witnessed an event unique in broadcasting history—the first production featuring scripts *not* written by human beings. The "author" was the TX-o computer. The scripts were included in the hour-long show already referred to, "The Thinking Machine," appearing on the television network of the Columbia Broadcasting System. They consisted of three Western playlets acted in pantomime, performed in a slightly surrealistic manner, and based on the following traditional situation:

> The robber has returned to the hideout, put the bag of money in the corner of the shack, gloated over it, and now sits drinking at a rickety table. He occasionally checks his gun and fidgets. As he goes to the corner to gloat over the money again, the sheriff—unseen—creeps past the window toward the door. The robber nervously checks his gun. The sheriff throws open the door and they see each other. For an instant the sheriff waits. The question is: will the robber surrender?

Douglas Ross and Harrison Morse of M.I.T.'s Electronics Systems Laboratory put this problem to TX-o as part of a television-script-writing program known as SAGA II. Pre-

Douglas Ross and Harrison Morse of M.I.T. programmed the TX-o computer to write Western scripts. Here they are shown during a rehearsal for "The Thinking Machine," the Columbia Broadcasting System's television show on computers.

paring the program represented another "first." Never before had computer specialists struggled with the hectic job of meeting a script deadline, thus obtaining a firsthand notion of the difficulties confronting television producers. It took the investigators about two months to develop SAGA II, much of the work running into the late nighttime hours. The computer required about two minutes to turn out a script. Here is the "as broadcast" version of the first televised playlet ("MS," "CU," and "LS" stand for medium shot, close-up, and long shot, respectively):

MUSIC UP
FILM
MS ROBBER PEERING THRU WINDOW OF SHACK
CU ROBBER'S FACE
MS ROBBER ENTERING SHACK
CU ROBBER SEES WHISKEY BOTTLE ON TABLE
CU SHERIFF OUTSIDE SHACK
MS ROBBER SEES SHERIFF

```
beginnt1+23| X
  gun is in right hand
  money is in left hand

nt1+23|              tra bwr                    tra bwh

begin t0
  gun is in right hand
  money is in left hand
  drink is on table
  robber is in corner
  right hand is on robber
  left hand is on robber
  holster is on robber
  bottle is on table

  right hand has gun
  left hand has money
  holster has nothing

t00
  gun is in corner

t01
```

Actual sample of computer-written Western script, showing how the TX-o types out each detailed step of the
action.

> LS SHERIFF IN DOORWAY OVER SHOULDER OF ROBBER,
>   BOTH DRAW
> MS SHERIFF DRAWING GUN
> LS SHOOTING IT OUT. ROBBER GETS SHOT
> MS SHERIFF PICKING UP MONEY BAGS
> MS ROBBER STAGGERING
> MS ROBBER DYING. FALLS ACROSS TABLE, AFTER TRYING
>   TO TAKE LAST SHOT AT SHERIFF
> MS SHERIFF WALKING THRU DOORWAY WITH MONEY
> MS OF ROBBER'S BODY, NOW STILL, LYING ACROSS TABLE
>   TOP. CAMERA DOLLIES BACK

Now the above material is not what the TX-o actually
wrote. In contrast to most real-life writers, it had a limited
capacity for handling the King's English and no previous
experience to draw on. Working without the benefits of
a higher education, it was forced to go through the pains-

Classic Western situation—
sheriff confronts robber . . .

robber hits sheriff (only a flesh
wound, of course) . . .

sheriff hits robber . . .

and gets his man.

taking process of typing out the entire script in a kind of step-by-step babytalk. The fourteen as-broadcast lines are a condensed version of more than a hundred computer lines. The condensation is roughly the sort of thing you would do if you read "one plus one plus one plus one plus one" and simply wrote down "5." This is how part of an original TX-o script looks as it comes off the automatic typewriter:

SHERIFF:

    the sheriff is at the window
    sheriff sees robber
    robber sees sheriff
    go to door
    wait
    open door
    sheriff sees robber
    go thru door
    robber sees sheriff
    go to window

ROBBER:

    take gun from holster with right hand
    aim
    fire
    SHERIFF NICKED

SHERIFF:

    take gun from holster with right hand
    aim
    fire
    ROBBER NICKED

ROBBER:

    wait
    aim
    fire
    MISSED

SHERIFF:

   aim

   fire

ROBBER HIT

   blow out barrel

   put gun down at door

   go to table

   pick up glass with right hand . . .

Before turning out such copy the TX-o required an elementary education, the SAGA II program. Like all computer programs, this one had to be extremely specific. The machine had to be told every rule of the game in explicit detail. Every word in its vocabulary, for example, is coded into a unique binary number and stored in its memory unit —and the program must be written so that only certain combinations of word-numbers are allowed. If 111, 110, 101, 001, and 011 stand for "robber," "right hand," "gun," "takes," and "holster"—then 111-001-101-011-110 is a permissible sequence: "robber takes gun (from) holster (with) right hand." But 101-001-111-011-110, or "gun takes robber (from) holster (with) right hand," is a forbidden sequence.

Make no mistake about it, the program has to consider all possibilities. The statement "robber puts gun into holster" seems straightforward enough. But at an early stage in the development of SAGA II, Ross and Morse neglected to make it clear that the sheriff is to put his gun into *his* holster, a point which is obvious to us but hardly to a machine. So in one script the TX-o had the sheriff slipping his gun into the robber's holster, and it was necessary to revise the program so that such a blunder could not occur again. (This script was one of the three produced on the television show, and very few viewers noticed the sheriff's unconventional maneuver.)

The TX-o follows instructions in developing its plots. To start, the control unit refers to a memory location

"Enter Robber," and then proceeds to successive steps which describe the robber's actions as he appears outside the shack and then comes in: go to window, go to door, go through door, close door, go to corner, put money down. Up to this point every script is the same. But now we come to the first "switch," a programming feature so designed that various alternative or branching paths are possible. Among other things, the robber may go to the window and look out and then go to the table, or he may go to the table directly.

One important feature of the SAGA II program is its unpredictability. You cannot tell in advance which one of these alternatives the program will select, because it does the equivalent of rolling a pair of dice. It instructs the TX-o to change the number in its arithmetic unit in such a way that it generates a random number—and the value of the number determines what happens next. If the number happens to be larger than a particular value, the control unit refers to a memory location where the go-to-the-table instruction is stored. Otherwise the unit looks up memory locations storing other alternatives.

The machine also selects alternatives randomly at later stages, but the odds may be weighted in various ways. The program specifies that when the sheriff first appears he is outside the shack and peers in through the window. If he sees the robber inside, he can either advance directly to the attack (entering through the door) or look to see what is in the robber's hand. Common sense dictates that he look first, but doing the right thing every time may lead to dull plots and is not a human characteristic in any case. So the appropriate switch is adjusted according to the probability that the sheriff will advance without taking a precautionary look once out of every five times.

Another "probability" switch determines the sheriff's actions if the robber's hand has a gun in it, holds something else, or is empty. Special switches control what happens when the time comes to shoot it out. When one man shoots he may hit, nick, or miss his adversary. A hit means a kill. A nick means wounding without killing, and the wounded man will naturally miss more often than he did before—a situation which is duly allowed for. Shooting efficiency is also affected by alcohol, so an "inebriation factor" is included in the SAGA II program. Every time the robber takes a drink, the odds increase that he will miss when he shoots. Furthermore, a swig out of the bottle increases his chances of missing more than a drink out of a glass.

In all there are more than thirty switches, each having two or three alternative positions. So the chances that the TX-o will write the identical script twice are extremely small. The three Western playlets produced on the television show were selected from about fifty different scripts. Sometimes the sheriff won, sometimes the robber. In one case, both were killed. The program is prepared so that the two men are on a par as far as shooting ability is concerned, assuming both are sober. But the robber may drink before the shooting starts. The sheriff only goes to the bottle after the battle, and that makes all the difference. As a reward for being virtuous at the right time, he wins in three out of four scripts.

The ending of one script was definitely offbeat. The rule is that the winner goes to the corner, picks up the money, leaves the shack, and takes one last look through the window. This time, however, a mix-up occurred. The sheriff thought he had won and went through the scheduled actions. But the robber was not dead. He was supposed to follow the winner's routine, which meant, first of all, getting the money. Since the money was not in the corner, he reached through the window and took it from the sheriff's hand. Then he left the shack and joined the sheriff at the window. The script ended with both men alive and on the outside looking into an empty room.

This is the closest the machine came to writing an "original" script. Apparently nothing was wrong with the circuits or the program at the time, and it is still a mystery why the sheriff thought he had won. Incidentally, a more sophisticated program could be written if a strong enough demand existed. For example, you could arrange things so that the sheriff and robber shouted at one another during the fight, and uttered dying words and victory soliloquies. The machine requires about fifty-five hundred instructions to turn out pantomimes. A program for writing dialogue as well as action might call for at least two to three times more instructions, but it is certainly within the realm of possibility.

SAGA II was not part of a project to replace human writers of Westerns with machines, even if someone with sufficient funds considered that desirable or profitable. Ross has stated his objectives precisely: "It is not a demonstration that authors are being pushed into oblivion. And the chances of ever creating an electronic Euripides or a transistorized Tolstoy are infinitely negligible. . . . We wanted to show in an entertaining manner that one highly important aspect of artificial intelligence is that it must obey the proper rules in the proper way. We also wanted to experiment with a situation that might lead the computer to break the rules, but break them in a natural way. This led to the introduction of the inebriation factor. There is no black magic about the behavior of computers."

The SAGA II experiment illustrates how swiftly things are moving in computer research. It would have been impossible to write a horse-opera program, and in a hurry at that, without a considerable store of accumulated knowledge. Such work is part of an intensive effort to explore the capabilities of the new machines, to obtain a clearer idea of what they can and cannot do. We know that they can write crude scenarios, though they may never write great plays. We also know they can compose music of a sort. Using a program whose basic principles do not differ radically from those applied in SAGA II, two investigators at the University of Illinois' School of Music have instructed the ILLIAC computer to produce fragmentary scores and improvise within limits. The result, an "ILLIAC Suite for String Quartet," cannot compare with the compositions of even third-rate musicians.

But how far can we go? What are the machines' limitations—and why? We are devising new tests in a new area, writing out programs which will enable the computer to advance beyond its present achievements and come closer to the achievements of the human mind. On the theoretical side, which will be considered in later chapters, we can expect to learn more and more about the nature of thought processes. On the practical side are a host of problems which will not be solved until we make our machines behave more cleverly. This is not a task for theorists only. The engineers have moved in, and industry already has its "Departments of Artificial Intelligence" and "Synthetic Intelligence Sections." There is even a ten-dollar word for the field, "intellectronics."

A major part of the field involves the formidable problem of dealing with technical-information bottlenecks. At present our situation resembles that of the driver caught in a Sunday traffic jam and wondering why anyone ever bothered to invent the automobile in the first place. Similar thoughts may cross the mind of the investigator who writes a paper which contributes its bit to the 60 million pages of scientific literature published every year. The problem is the subject of a recent article by Helen Brownson of the National Science Foundation, a 10-page survey devoted to "the mechanized handling of the ideas, concepts and techniques embodied in the texts and illustrations of scientific documents." Mrs. Brownson, director of the Foundation-supported projects in this area, covers a wide range of studies under way in the United States as well as in the Soviet Union and other countries.

For example, take the automatic indexing of printed material. Articles and books can be put on magnetic tapes and fed into a computer, filling its memory unit with words coded as binary digits. Then a program tells the machine to scan its memory for specified key words, specified sets of binary digits, which are needed to compile name and subject indexes. Computers have been used to prepare a Bible concordance and to index the Dead Sea Scrolls and the complete works of the thirteenth-century theologian St. Thomas Aquinas. The last job, which was done by IBM machines, so impressed the Vatican that Pope John XXIII conferred the Grand Cross of the Equestrian Order of St. Sylvester on Thomas and Arthur Watson, the two top executives of the organization.

FOSDIC 2, a file-searching machine developed by the National Bureau of Standards, sorts weather information. It scans microfilm reels which contain images of punch cards representing wind direction, temperature, and other data, and can examine several thousand cards a minute. The machine is located at the Air Weather Service offices in Asheville, North Carolina, whose files contain more than 300 million cards. Electronic searching equipment is also at work checking on new applications at the U.S. Patent Office, keeping tabs on tens of thousands of chemical compounds for industrial and drug companies, and helping the harried staffs of large libraries.

Machines may also play a role in summarizing or abstracting material. An article is first "rewritten" in computer language on magnetic tape with patterns of magnetized spots coded to represent individual words, and the entire text is stored in the memory unit. The machine, following specific instructions, begins sorting out and classifying. First it examines the coded information of binary-digit words, discards the most common everyday words, and performs various other operations. Then it prepares a sort of small-scale census or frequency list of the remaining words, counting the number of times each word appears. Finally, it examines all the sentences in the article to find which one contains the largest number of high-frequency words—and types it out as the required abstract.

IBM investigators have been studying this procedure for several years. In one experiment they fed a computer an article about nerve chemistry. The article contained a total of 2,326 words, 571 of which were classified as "noncommon." The computer compiled a frequency list showing that the 39 most-used noncommon words occurred 478 times and, on the basis of the list, selected the following sentence as the most significant in the article from an abstracting point of view: "It is reasonable to suppose that the tranquilizing drugs counteract the inhibitory effect of excessive adrenalin or serotonin or some related inhibitor in the human nervous system." This sentence is a reasonably good summary of the new ideas in the article, and similar experiments have been tried on articles up to about five thousand words long.

More ambitious projects include a question-asking study being conducted at the Ramo-Wooldridge Laboratories in Canoga Park, California. The idea here is to start with the investigator himself, to find out what he wants to know and how he would go about looking for it. The first step is to make up an experimental "library" consisting of a hundred articles on nuclear physics selected over a ten-year period from the leading American journal in the field, the *Physical Review*. All the complete articles are coded onto magnetic tape and stored in a computer. Then a group of scientists specified how they would search the articles for answers to fifty highly technical questions—for example, how does charge polarization within a nucleus affect the coulomb scattering of charged particles by that nucleus?

In this case, the machine would be instructed to deliver to the questioner all articles meeting the following specification: they would contain the phrase "charge polarization" or "charge distribution," and also one or more of the words "scattering," "scattered," or "scatter." Notice that the aim is to achieve direct and natural communications between man and machine. The machine does no indexing or classifying. It makes no attempt to analyze the articles until it receives a clearly stated request. Then it "thumbs" through its stored articles and identifies the ones which meet the investigator's requirements. Tests indicate that this approach may be one of the most promising yet considered.

It should be emphasized that projects of this sort are still in the preliminary stage and still face serious obstacles. Not all of the obstacles, by the way, are a matter of improved circuitry and engineering skill. In fact, the most complex of them are social rather than technical. Indexing, abstracting, and all literature-searching methods are only parts of a much broader problem—namely, to design a more effective system for the international flow and distribution of information, scientific and otherwise. That is a communications problem, a problem of social structuring, and it will not be solved by computers alone.

But computer research has a good deal to offer, as the Brownson–National Science Foundation survey indicates: "The possible consequences of such research are of the greatest importance for science. At the very least the research should result in increased understanding of the complex processes of communications among scientists—and in improvements in the means for accomplishing such communications and for consulting the record of accumulated scientific knowledge. It may also, however, lead to completely new ways, only dimly foreseen at this time, of using machines to supplement human intelligence in information and communication processes."

Electronic translation is another area that may be classified under the heading "artificial intelligence." About a dozen American research groups at university and industrial laboratories are doing active work in this area, and the demand for more investigators is increasing steadily. As far as practical objectives are concerned, the major emphasis is on translating from Russian to English. According to one estimate, our military and intelligence requirements can be satisfied by translating only six-tenths of one per cent of Russian publications. Yet to meet even this modest requirement we would have to translate at least five times as much material as we are actually translating today.

The general idea of using machines to do the job is not new. One of the earliest notions along these lines is described in a 1910 issue of *Popular Mechanics*. The magazine carried an item concerning the novel suggestion of an unnamed Michigan inventor, "an interpreting telephone" which would convert English, for example, into another language: "Attached to the side of an ordinary telephone receiver is a box in which different languages are stored. If the man answering the phone is Chinese, he will move the indicator opposite the Chinese language, and then some mysterious mechanism yet to be designed will receive the English words coming over the wire and convert them into Chinese."

Investigators currently engaged in the task of putting such ideas into practice smile wryly when they come to the phrase, "some mysterious mechanism yet to be designed." The entire history of electronic translation is a record of efforts to transform that vague statement into a working system. The first organized attempt to go beyond scientific daydreaming occurred shortly after World War II. Andrew

Booth, a mathematician at the University of London, developed an elementary but promising program for a general-purpose computer. In effect, he instructed the machine to do what a naïve, plodding human translator might do—namely, provide a straightforward and unesthetic word-by-word translation.

First of all, the machine needed a dictionary, a 100-word French-English dictionary in one experiment. Here is a rough idea of the system Booth devised. Each French word is represented as a pattern of holes on a punch card, which also includes a pattern representing one of the possible English translations of the word. It is stored in the memory unit in the form of a code number, say 1101011. Now imagine that the problem is to translate a French sentence including this word. Since the word becomes 1101011 in computer language, the machine searches for that number in its dictionary. If it finds the number in a particular memory location, it refers to another location for the English equivalent and types out the translation. In such operations it functions mainly as a word-matching or number-matching device.

Suppose the word-number is not in the computer's dictionary. The machine is not defeated yet. It has one more trick left which may or may not work. For purposes of illustration, let us assume that it is translating from English to French and comes across the word "calling." It chops off the last letter of the word, leaving "callin" and looks that up in its memory. Still frustrated, it continues the chopping-off and looking-up process until only four letters remain. That leaves "call." If the dictionary does not include this word, the machine gives up and tosses the problem back to its programmers, simply typing out "calling" untranslated. But if the word is included, the machine goes back and examines the whole set of chopped-off letters. It consults a grammatical appendix, finds that the "ing" ending may be used to make a noun from a verb, and translates accordingly.

The original Booth translating program was rather crude. It converted articulate French sentences into a hideous version of broken English, inferior even to clumsy efforts of a tourist who does not speak the language. As one sarcastic commentator pointed out, it was roughly equivalent to mangling the first line of the Twenty-third Psalm, "The Lord is my shepherd; I shall not want," into "Lord my shepherd no I will lack." But it was a beginning, and, furthermore, the objective was to translate scientific reports, which may not present such difficulties. For one thing, their style is seldom of so high a literary quality that they would suffer appreciably in a reasonably good machine translation. Also, investigators have specialized problems and vocabularies, and may be able to extract sense from computer-typed sentences which would be meaningless to the layman.

A more advanced program was displayed about eight years ago during a special press conference held at the New York headquarters of IBM. This demonstration involved translating from Russian into English. Reporters, mathematicians, and company officials watched as a girl operator typed information into a large electronic computer, which read Russian sentences such as the following: MYEZHDU-NARODNOYE PONYIMANYIYE YAVLYAYETSYA VAZHNIM FAKTOROM V RYESHYENYIYI POLY-ITYICHYESSKYIX VOPROSOV. The computer, lights blinking and motors whirring, hesitated for less than nine seconds, during which time it performed some 60,000 operations. Then it typed the English version: "International understanding constitutes an important factor in decision of political questions."

The translating system for this demonstration was devised by Leon Dostert and Paul Garvin of Georgetown

University in Washington, D.C. They prepared a vocabulary of 250 Russian words which were represented on punch cards as in the original Booth method. But some of the cards contained two possible English equivalents instead of merely one. There were also special punched-in codes which represented certain rules of language structure and, among other things, helped the machine to distinguish one word from another of similar form. The information required a total of 216,000 binary digits in the computer's memory unit. Next came a deck of punch cards carrying the 2,400 instructions of the translating program, which set up the machine for handling a number of Russian sentences especially selected to fall within the linguistic scope of the program.

The system included features which went somewhat beyond the straight dictionary approach. For example, take the following two Russian sentences and their English equivalents:

KACHYESTVO   UGLYA   OPRYEDYELYAYETSYA
The quality of   coal   is determined by

KALORYIYNOSTJU
calory content.

VYELYICHYINA UGLA   OPRYEDYELYAYETSYA
Magnitude of angle   is determined by

OTNOSHYENYIYEM   DLYINI   DUGI K RADYIUSU
the relation   of length   of arc to radius.

Notice the second words in the above Russian sentences. They both have the same basic root, "ugl," but the ending determines whether the translation shall be "coal" or "angle." So it is not sufficient simply to chop off the endings and look up the root in the dictionary. Since the endings are all-important and completely alter the meaning, additional instructions are required to take care of such situations.

It would have been possible to store "uglya" and "ugla" as separate words in the memory unit. The Garvin-Dostert program, however, employed a more refined procedure. Only the root was stored, together with the alternative English translations. The machine looked up "ugl" and then examined the ending to decide which of the two meanings should be used in translating the sentences. It was also capable of taking into account, to a limited degree, differences in Russian and English word orders. Under suitable circumstances, it reversed pairs of words on the basis of a special set of instructions.

As far as research is concerned, the New York demonstration served a useful purpose. It indicated that linguistic rules may be expressed in terms which a computer can follow and apply in routine operation. Investigators were properly cautious at the time. They pointed out that it is one thing to translate selected sentences—and something else again to tackle full-length documents prepared with no regard for the limitations of computers or the men who write computer programs. On the other hand, they expected advances to come more rapidly than has actually been the case. According to one 1954 report, "within a few years the system may greatly increase communication, particularly in technical subjects, by making translation quick, accurate and easy."

That prediction was a bit on the overoptimistic side. We have not yet reached the stage of quick, accurate, and easy translations. Nothing is easy in this field. Some indication of where we stand now was presented to Congress at a recent hearing on mechanical translation before the House Committee on Science and Astronautics. IBM investigators took the concluding remarks of a speech Khrushchev delivered to the Supreme Soviet of the U.S.S.R. and inspired by the U-2 plane incident. They offered two versions to contrast the abilities of electronic and human translators. Here is the human version of the last two paragraphs:

> We began the seven-year plan well, comrades. Production plans are being fulfilled and overfulfilled, reserves in the national economy are growing, the productivity of labor is increasing. The great will of the people, their selfless labor, the socialist competition of millions are a reliable guarantee of the successful accomplishment and overfulfillment of the seven-year plan, of the further advance of the economy, of the development of science and culture, of the improvement in the welfare of the Soviet people.
>
> While speaking about successes, we should always critically examine all aspects of our activity, we should not rest content with what has been achieved, we should constantly be concerned about complete utilization of the great reserves we have and of the possibilities for the powerful development of all branches of the national economy.

The following translation is what the computer made of Khrushchev's remarks:

> Seven-year school/plan we began good, comrade. Are carried out and overfulfill industrial plan, grow storage in national economy, increase productivity labor. Great will people, it/its selfless labor, socialist competition millions correct guarantee successful accomplishment and overfulfillment seven-year plan, further rise economics, development science and culture, increase welfare Soviet people.
>
> Talking about successes, we always should critical look at all side our activity, not calm on reached, constant care about that in order to completely use having by us great reserves and possibility for high-power development all branch national economy.

For all its imperfections, this version is impressive when you consider that it was produced by a system of electronic hardware. As far as our reactions are concerned, translating machines are something like talking animals. The amazing fact is not how well or how poorly they do it, but that they do it at all. We are far from achieving polished computer translations. On the other hand, it should be re-emphasized that the aim is not literary quality, and certainly not the handling of political speeches, which may be somewhat ambiguous to start with. Current efforts are focused on the more precise statements of scientific reports. A computer or a scientist may convey important data without using perfect English, particularly when the person reading the results is a specialist thoroughly familiar with the general drift of the contents.

With this situation in mind, investigators have made notable advances in their drive to provide useful Russian-to-English translations. They have analyzed a large number of technical papers and compiled carefully selected vocabularies in metallurgy, aeronautics, organic chemistry, electronics, and other areas. They have designed memory units capacious enough to hold thousands of words, roots, and endings. They have attained remarkable speeds. Skilled professional translators trained in science, and we do not have many of them, may average perhaps 2,600 words a day. A fast computer can turn out the same number of words in three minutes, and there is no reason why that rate cannot be increased ten times or more.

The fundamental question is how much sense the words make. In this field one good job produced in a day or two may be considerably more valuable than any number of third-rate jobs produced in a fraction of that time. The accuracy and practical value of available computer translations can be debated, but there is little argument on one point. No one is satisfied with present results. When it comes to quality of output, electronic translators are not yet capable of competing with human translators; they are simply not in the same league. We must check up on them to make sure that they have not garbled or failed to convey completely the important contents of technical papers.

One of the biggest problems concerns words with many meanings. To take an extreme example, look up the word "run" in your dictionary. The one I have is medium-sized and lists 104 different meanings. The task of distinguishing among them was discussed at the Congressional hearings by Anthony Oettinger, a mathematician and linguist at Harvard University. He mentioned some fairly simple ways of programming a machine to tell whether the word is being used as a noun or a verb. For example, the odds are that it is a noun if it follows "a" or "the" and a verb if it follows "we" or "you." Machines can be instructed to operate on the basis of such rules.

But telling verbs from nouns is only the beginning of the problem. Many decisions must be made within the two broad classes. How can a machine select among such verbal usages as running for office, running aground, running through a list, running through with a sword, running into debt, running a blockade? And what about noun meanings—a run on a bank or in a stocking, the run of the grain in wood, a run of good luck, the run of the house? In every case the distinctions involve a great deal more than examining a single word, or even the word together with those preceding and following it. Selecting the proper meaning involves questions of context and the analysis of whole sentences.

We cannot yet instruct a machine to undertake such work—or to arrange all the words of a sentence in a correct order, another major problem in automatic translation. Advances of this sort must await the results of basic research in linguistics, long-range studies which are under way at a number of universities. Victor Yngve, director of the Mechanical Translation Group at M.I.T., is one of the investigators exploring certain aspects of the organization of sentences. He has prepared a program by which a machine, given a vocabulary and a set of grammatical rules and instructions for applying rules, can write sentences on its own. The sentences are simple, but the program provides rather subtle insights into language structure.

For instance, Yngve has discovered why we avoid certain ways of saying things and prefer others. Consider the following examples:

> If what going to a clearly not very adequately staffed school really means is little appreciated, we should be concerned.

> We should be concerned if there is little appreciation of what it really means to go to a school which clearly is not very adequately staffed.

The first of these sentences is awkward, and if you spoke that way as a practice, you would soon find yourself with no listeners. But coming to grips with the essential problem demands a precise analysis of this feeling of awkwardness.

When you utter the first part of a sentence, say a subordinate clause, you must and do keep in mind that it will be followed by a main clause, to conform with the conventions of the English language. While uttering the subject of the subordinate clause itself, you must also remember that it is to be followed by an appropriate verb or predicate. The first sentence above may require the speaker and the listener to keep track of up to eight such commitments. The second sentence requires only two or three because of alternative grammatical constructions which allow many of the commitments to be satisfied early in the sentence and before they "pile up" to a confusing extent.

Now psychologists have found that our immediate-memory span is about seven items. This finding is closely related to sentence structure and is based on experiments such as the following. Suppose that you are permitted to look for a few seconds only at cards with random words printed on them. If a card has three or four words, you will probably recall all of them without trouble. But the odds are that you will begin forgetting as the number of words approaches seven—and only exceptional persons can remember as many as eight or nine words. These tests show that memory is limited when it comes to rapid, on-the-spot storage capacity.

So expressions like the first of the above sentences are unwieldy for us because of something about the way our brains are built. Creatures with longer immediate-memory spans would have no trouble uttering or understanding such sentences. They would not consider the sentences at all awkward. From these and other observations Yngve concludes: "It appears that the syntax of English is not an endless catalog of whimsical complications, although there are some relics of the past. Neither does English appear to be an abstract formal system, on a par with certain elegant mathematical notations. Instead, it is a particularly well engineered instrument of communication, with many ingenious innovations to adapt it to the capabilities of its users and to circumvent as much as possible the limitations of human memory."

The central point is that language can be a rich field for scientific exploration. Like the physical universe it obeys basic laws, some of which we know. But the deepest and most important laws remain to be discovered. Another thing is clear. The laws of language are subtly related to the way we think and to the workings of the brain. In the ultimate sense linguistics is a study of the human mind, of human behavior. A language is a set of customs and habits and traditions, an entire way of life.

From this standpoint, the role of the computer has a special significance. It furnishes a first-rate example of the complex interplay of practical and theoretical studies. Studies designed to improve automatic translating are helping to spur work in linguistics, although the field was expanding a decade before the coming of the machines. But in the very process of applying research findings to the translation problem we are accumulating more knowledge about the nature of thought. It is a good guess that linguistic research will assume greater and greater importance in our efforts to understand intelligence, artificial and otherwise.

CHAPTER 8

GAMES, STRATEGIES, LEARNING

Oₙₑ OF THE STRANGEST GAMES in chess history took place in Vienna nearly two hundred years ago at the Royal Palace of the Empress Maria Theresa. An attendant wheeled a weird piece of furniture into the room. It consisted of a life-sized dummy dressed up as a Turk, complete with turban and black moustache, and seated behind a large chest with a chessboard on the top. There was polite applause. Then Baron Wolfgang von Kempelen, Aulic Counselor on Mechanics to the Royal Chamber and inventor extraordinary, stepped forward and introduced his new Automaton Chess Player. Would someone like to play a game with the machine?

The audience was sophisticated, amused—and skeptical. No one stepped forward. Ah, yes; but, of course, people could look inside. The Baron proceeded to open one of the three front doors of the chest, revealing a system of levers and wheels and shafts and clockwork mechanisms. Next he opened a rear door directly behind the machinery, as the attendant held a candle so that the light shone through the maze of parts and could be seen by spectators on the front side. After closing the rear door, he opened the two other front doors and two drawers containing chess pieces. He then reopened the rear door, wheeled the chest around, and lifted the Turk's robe revealing more machinery. Now the audience was more impressed. They could see no place for a human being to hide.

The Baron had a few more things to do. He took a key out of his pocket and wound up the machine. He also removed a small box from the chest, placed it on the floor, and explained that it provided the secret energy to move the Turk. Now would someone like to play a game? A guest stood in front of the Automaton, which turned its head from side to side as if scanning the board and contemplating a subtle strategy. Its hand reached out, grasped a pawn, and moved it two squares forward to execute a standard opening.

This was too much for one old lady. She rose from her chair, muttered something unrecorded, crossed herself hastily, and retired to another part of the room. The game was on, to the accompaniment of whirring and clicking sounds from inside the chest. When the guest's queen was threatened, the Turk bowed his head twice. He bowed three times to announce check. Once the rattled guest made an illegal move, and the Turk, shaking his head disapprovingly, put the offending piece back in place and made a penalty move of his own. Every ten moves or so the Baron rewound the machine.

History does not register the name of the Turk's first opponent or the winner of the game. According to all indications, however, the "machine" almost certainly won. It was a masterfully designed hoax with trick drawers, fake machinery, ingenious secret compartments, and a highly skilled chess player tucked away inside. The chess-playing automata of modern times have not attained such a high level of ability. But they are not hoaxes. They are electronic computers, any one of the large general-purpose machines in university and industrial laboratories. They obey to the letter instructions which we prepare for them, and their deficiencies can be traced directly to deficiencies in our programs.

Von Kempelen's Automaton Chess Player created a sensation. It baffled hundreds of thousands of persons during European and American tours, lost a very small proportion of its games (including one game which it lost on purpose to Napoleon whose play has been described by one chess expert as "beneath criticism"), and earned considerable money for its owners before being destroyed by a Philadelphia fire in 1854. Investigators working on genuine automata today are not interested in melodrama, mystification, or sideshows and profits. To them it is a matter of accepting a challenge. They want to know just how far they can go with a computer. They want to explore the possibilities of artificial intelligence to the limit. In the process, they may also gain a deeper understanding of natural thinking machines such as the human brain.

These points are emphasized in a recent report from the Rand Corporation in Santa Monica, California, an organization concerned with top-level defense strategies among other things: "Chess is the intellectual game par excellence. Without a chance device to obscure the contest, it pits two intellects against each other in a situation so complex that neither can hope to understand it completely, but sufficiently amenable to analysis that each can hope to out-think his opponent. The game is sufficiently deep and subtle in its implications to have supported the rise of professional players, and to have allowed a deepening analysis through 200 years of intensive study and play without becoming exhausted or barren. Such characteristics mark chess as a natural arena for attempts at mechanization. If you could devise a successful chess machine, one would seem to have penetrated to the core of human intellectual endeavor."

The evolution of automatic chess players is a phenomenon of the twentieth century. A leader in this development has been Claude Shannon of M.I.T., who also pioneered in the logic of circuits and other basic areas. More than a decade ago Shannon, a skilled chess amateur himself, began working at home to explore methods of mechanizing the game. Among his inventions was a machine enclosed in a metal cabinet about the size of a small tea table and including some 250 relay switches. Named Caissac, after Caissa the goddess of chess, it was a simple-minded but honest automaton.

A special chessboard was built into the top of the cabinet. A wire ran from an electrical contact on each square to the circuits inside, so that the machine could tell whether the square was empty or occupied. It recognized positions by unique pairs of numbers or addresses. Starting at the lower left-hand corner of the board, the eight "rank," or horizontal, rows were numbered from 0 to 7. The "file," or vertical rows, were identified in the same manner:

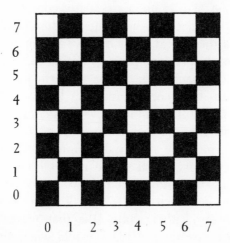

Thus, the upper left-hand square was simply 7,0 to Caissac, the lower right-hand corner was 0,7—and so on. The white pieces were represented as follows: 1 is a pawn, 2 a knight, 3 a bishop, 4 a rook, 5 a queen, and 6 a king. The same numbers with minus signs in front of them stood for the corresponding black pieces. The code $-2,7,1$ meant that the black knight is on the second square from the left in the top horizontal row.

Caissac had a relay memory large enough to hold the elementary rules of chess. It distinguished between legal and illegal moves, did additions and subtractions to compute the distances between pieces, and devised various moves depending on the tactics of its human opponent. It indicated its plays by flashing appropriate lights located on each one of the squares. The machine played only simple end games where it had an advantage of one piece, say, a rook and king to opponent's king. (Incidentally, a machine which played nothing but this single game was constructed as far back as 1914 by a Spanish mathematician, Torres y Quevedo.) It always won, since in such games checkmate can be achieved no matter what the opponent does and the play is not particularly complicated.

Shannon did not stop with the building of Caissac. He published a theoretical study of how a computer could be programmed to play complete games of chess, and practically all subsequent work on the problem has been based essentially on the general principles he discussed. In the first place, for all its complexity, chess shares an important property with a number of much simpler games. It is what mathematicians call "strictly determined." That is, a perfect strategy exists which would always lead to the same result. It has been proved that if two perfect players were matched against each other, one of three things would always happen. Either white (the first player to move) would win every time, or black would win every time, or every game would be a draw.

Our proofs fail us when it comes to showing which of

these three possibilities is the correct one. But there is a hint of the actual state of affairs. Studies of tournament games and experience accumulated over many years indicate that chess, like ticktacktoe, would always end in a draw, assuming that the opponents played perfectly. For example, in the famous 1927 world championship match between Capablanca and Alekhine 25 out of 34 games were tied. In any case, the main point is that one and only one of the possibilities holds—and that if we could play the game perfectly, there would be no point in playing at all.

The game is worth our time, simply because it is much too complicated to analyze completely. In a typical game the opponents will each move about forty times before one of them resigns, so that there is a grand total of 10^{120} possible variations (that is, a number represented by writing 120 zeros after the digit 1) to be explored. No brain, living or electronic, could begin to undertake such a task. A computer capable of examining a thousand billion billion variations a second, and that is far beyond the dreams of even the most optimistic investigators, would still take more than 10^{91} years to calculate its move—which is enormously longer than the age of the universe.

This is one of the reasons skeptics put forward in arguing that no machine will ever be able to play perfect chess. The argument is valid, but misses the point. The ultimate goal is not to program a computer to play perfectly, but merely to play as well as or perhaps better than the best human players. That is a somewhat restricted goal, to be sure. To achieve it certain compromises are necessary, as Shannon has recognized: "We resign ourselves . . . to having the machine play a reasonably skillful game, admitting occasional moves that may not be the best. This, of course, is precisely what human players do."

In one approach you can tell the machine to look only

a few moves ahead instead of exploring every position in great depth. There are problems here, too. A typical chess position has thirty-two possible moves by the player whose turn is up, and thirty-two possible replies by his opponent. So that means 1,024 different combinations must be examined to look ahead two moves. Looking ahead four moves, two by each player, involves 1,048,576 combinations; looking ahead six moves involves 1,073,741,824 combinations; and so on. It is clear that the practical limits of examining positions in depth depend on the speed of the machine and how long you are willing to wait for it to figure out each move.

But examining positions is not enough. They must also be compared, and that means the machine must have criteria which it can use as a basis for judgments. To do this it can draw on the results of human experience. For example, there are certain rule-of-thumb standards which help players decide whether or not an exchange of different pieces is a good bargain. Generally speaking a queen is worth about nine pawns, a rook five, and a bishop or knight three. Over-all positions and moves may also be evaluated in pawn units. If the moving of one piece exposes the opponent's king to check by another piece, the result is what is known as a "discovered check." The American master Reuben Fine has termed this tactic "the divebomber of the chessboard," and it may be worth two or three pawns.

Another important feature of any given position is mobility. A player's ability to defeat or forestall his opponent's attacks and launch varied attacks of his own depends to an appreciable extent on how free he is to move his pieces. A machine can be programmed to count the number of possible moves available to it in a particular position, count the opponent's possible moves, and compare the two totals. It would then proceed to evaluate its mobility on the basis of the fact that an advantage of ten moves is roughly equivalent to an extra pawn. These are some of the factors which may be calculated in arriving at chess strategies.

So much for theory. How do these principles work out in practice? The first attempt to apply Shannon's ideas in programming a large electronic computer took place in 1956 at the Los Alamos Scientific Laboratory. Five investigators worked with MANIAC I, one of the computers constructed according to the design of John von Neumann and his associates at the Institute for Advanced Study in Princeton. The Los Alamos team decided on a program which would permit the machine to look four moves ahead (two moves for each player). MANIAC I was fast for its day, but not fast enough to cope with regular chess at that depth. It would have taken an average of about an hour to consider the possibilities and make a move.

To speed things up, the investigators turned to a "scaled down" version of chess. They used a board with thirty-six instead of sixty-four squares, eliminated two pieces and two pawns on each side, and introduced a few other simplifications. That reduced the average time for a move to about twelve minutes. MANIAC I identified positions and pieces by means of a code comparable to that devised for Shannon's Caissac. It had only two criteria to go on. It evaluated combinations of moves by calculating mobility and "material advantage," that is, the comparative values of pieces exchanged in possible captures and recaptures. It was not wired to a chessboard like Caissac, but simply typed out its plays for the information of opponents who moved the pieces accordingly.

MANIAC I took part in only three games. In the first game, which was scheduled to check the program, it played itself (white won). This trial revealed a number of weaknesses, including a "mortal fear of checks" so that the machine would sacrifice practically anything to avoid such positions. Equipped with an improved program, it was ready for game No. 2. The opponent was an "outsider," Martin Kruskal of Princeton University, whose chess rating was considered high enough so that he had to give the machine his queen as a handicap.

The game ran for more than ten hours. After about fifteen moves Kruskal started referring to the machine as "he" instead of "it." At one point MANIAC I had a chance of winning, but it made a weak and ultimately fatal move a while later. That left it with only one way to delay checkmate, the sacrifice of its queen. The machine deliberated for twenty minutes before making this play, which an official report of the event described as "heart-breaking." Kruskal eventually won on his thirty-eighth move. There was some consolation in the final game, however. This time the machine was pitted against a beginner with one week's experience—and won.

Three games were enough to indicate the limitations of the program. It is capable of enabling a general-purpose computer to beat a weak player or, more specifically, a person who has played only about twenty games. But the experiments were significant as a promising start. They demonstrated that some reasonable play is possible even with a relatively simple program. One investigator commented as follows on the pioneer studies: "With very little in the way of complexity, we have at least entered the arena of human play—we can beat a beginner." (By the way, Los Alamos workers later tried regular sixty-four-square chess on a faster machine, MANIAC II, and achieved comparable results.)

More advanced and more "human" programs have been prepared since then. There is something very unsubtle about examining every single possible combination, reasonable or not. It is a typical brute-force machine approach, a kind of bulldozing operation. To use a rough analogy, suppose you were surveying a few square miles of land for a likely home site. You would never tramp over the entire territory section by section, examine every quarter acre or so thoroughly, and then compare every section to arrive at a decision. The plan might be systematic, but it is also insane. We expect that a person in his right mind will avoid the unattractive places and look over the most promising sites only.

A human chess player proceeds in the same way. He discards the vast majority of combinations, concentrating on a few which seem to offer the best chances of success. Computers may work along similar lines. About four years ago Alex Bernstein, a mathematician and a very strong amateur player, developed an ingenious program for IBM's 704 model. Before every move the machine is instructed to survey the entire chessboard in detail, "asking about each square whether it is occupied, by whose man, whether it is attacked, whether it is defended, whether it can be occupied." Although this is the straight bulldozer approach, the full square-by-square analysis takes only about a tenth of a second.

The finesse begins at this stage. The 704 looks four moves ahead, but it does *not* look at all possible moves and combinations. For each of the four moves, it selects only seven alternatives for detailed investigation. Its criteria for selection are based on sound chess principles. First it asks: Is my king in check? If so, it lists appropriate moves—capturing the checking piece, moving the king away, interposing a piece between the king and the checking piece. If not, it asks the next question: Can I make any exchanges, and if so, will I gain by the play or should I move my man away? The machine is directed to ask these and six other questions in a definite order, and to stop its queries in any case as soon as it has found a maximum of seven plausible moves.

To begin with, the machine tests the first of the seven alternatives for its first move, producing a tentative new position on the board. Then it looks at things from its opponent's point of view, selecting *his* seven alternative replies on the basis of the same set of questions, and testing the first of them. Having done this, the machine shifts over to its own side of the board again to select its seven replies, and tests the first of them. Then it goes through the same process for its opponent's second reply. Working backward now, it evaluates all consequences of the remaining six of its original seven countermoves on the basis of pieces to be gained, defense of king, mobility, and control of important squares. The machine operates in this way until it has analyzed some 2,800 different combinations before it finally actually makes a move. But the significant point is that these are combinations selected from a possible total of more than a million. About eight minutes is required to make an average move, a bit more than double the average time allowed in tournament play.

The full program of some eight thousand instructions is represented in a deck of 330 punch cards, the information being transferred to a reel of magnetic tape and thence into the machine's memory. In an actual game you sit at the control console with a chessboard in front of you. If it is your play, you make your move on the board and then type out the move, which is conveyed to the computer via a punch card. You push a button, telling the machine you are ready. After about eight minutes, it types a diagram of the whole chessboard indicating its move. Bernstein does not know exactly how many games the 704 model has played. He has sent about thirty decks of programming cards to laboratories having the machine and has no records of the number of contests conducted elsewhere.

He himself has played four or five games, mainly to

check on the effectiveness of the instructions. Of special interest are two games in which the machine's opponent was Edward Lasker, the New York chess master. The first game was not really a game at all. Lasker was putting the program to the test and, during the play, purposely put six of his pieces in a position where the 704 could take them on its next move (if it was "smart" enough). He lost them all. Then he played to win and bested the machine within twenty moves. But later he commented: "I feel that when applied to a machine having sufficient speed and memory capacity, quite a strong game could be produced by Bernstein's program without changing its method in principle." As is, the program produces a "passable" amateur game.

Investigators are currently at work on approaches that come closer and closer to human chess-playing methods. For example, there is the research of Herbert Simon, Allen Newell, and J. Clifford Shaw of the Rand Corporation and the Carnegie Institute of Technology. Their program is rather more complex than Bernstein's, and certainly too complex to discuss here. But the net effect is to produce a new order of flexibility. Operating according to the program, Rand's JOHNNIAC follows the human policy of not always probing positions to the same depth.

The Viennese chess master, Richard Reti, once replied as follows when asked how many moves he usually looked ahead: "Oh, one—sometimes two." The point is that experts only examine certain situations in depth. Good amateurs rarely look more than twelve to sixteen moves ahead, when they encounter "forced variations," that is, positions in which the number of possible moves is quite restricted. World champions may look thirty to forty moves ahead in certain situations.

The extent of JOHNNIAC's foresight depends on the particular position involved. It may look only a few moves ahead as a rule. Generally when it probes in depth, it looks eight to eleven moves ahead, although it has been known to carry the process to as many as twenty-two moves. Furthermore, the program is designed so that criteria for evaluating positions are not always the same, and it does not analyze only seven plausible moves as stipulated in the Bernstein program. The computer analyzes all possible plausibilities. As a result, the Rand–Carnegie Tech investigators expected that each JOHNNIAC move would take one to ten hours.

Fortunately, it has not worked out that way. In about half a dozen games JOHNNIAC has taken from a minute to an hour for a move, but the average is about ten minutes, and play is generally completed within four hours. Here is how Simon summarizes the situation: "Our program is fairly impressive in the very opening play when center control and development are at issue. I think that at this stage we can rate it at the medium or grade-B amateur level. But after that, it isn't so good."

Prospects seem bright for a considerably higher level of electronic chess. For one thing, new computers will operate at even more spectacular speeds. Machines that can calculate a hundred and fifty or more times faster than JOHNNIAC are already in existence, which means that the average time for a move using the Rand–Carnegie Tech system would be reduced from ten minutes to about four seconds. (Los Alamos scientists had planned to try such an approach on their STRETCH computer, but the scheme has been shelved for higher-priority projects.)

Of course, the objective is not to make present programs faster but to sacrifice some of that speed for increasingly sophisticated programs. Suppose you wanted to modify the Bernstein program to look five instead of four moves ahead. On the 704 the average move would take 6½ hours, a figure which would drop to 2½ minutes or less with the fastest computers now available.

At present Simon and his associates are developing their program for more refined tactics. Among other things, they want to anticipate positions where the king may be threatened. Previous programs have gone into action only when the king is actually in check, which leaves the machine vulnerable to carefully laid traps. A "serious threats" subprogram which would tell the machine to avoid a check coming in two or three moves would produce a notably improved game. It would also require more complicated analysis and a correspondingly longer time to decide on appropriate moves.

But the most intriguing notion of all, and the one which might produce really high-grade chess, is to devise a program so that a computer will learn. If a good learning program were prepared, the problem of automaton chess would be solved—in theory, at least. It would be possible to put the machine off in a corner and let it play itself in a continuing "tournament." It might start off at a low-amateur level. But it would certainly ripen with age, like good wine. After a sufficient period it would accumulate sufficient chess knowledge to conquer the greatest living players. As a matter of fact, that might be our best bet for ending Russia's traditional domination of the game.

A chess automaton that learns is no longer considered out of the question. In fact there is already a hint of what may happen in a program worked out for another game, checkers. The potential, up-and-coming world's checker champion is neither a seasoned veteran who has been improving his play for years, nor an eight-year-old prodigy defeating his elders before hushed audiences. It is a machine, the general-purpose computer. Its program incorporates the same basic principles that make up a chess-playing program—the rules of the game, methods for identifying individual squares and pieces, ways of evaluating pieces (two kings being worth three men) and positions (mobility, possible gains and losses, and so on).

The program is based on the ideas of Arthur Samuel, a special consultant at IBM's Yorktown Heights laboratories in New York. Samuel has been called "one of the best of the old-fashioned (that is, nonelectronic) brains in the IBM research department," an appropriate designation when you consider what he is up to. His regular working day is devoted to company problems of immediate concern, his spare time to the study of machines that learn. He chose checkers, because it is a great deal less complicated than chess and you can therefore concentrate chiefly on the learning process. It involves simpler moves, thirty-two instead of sixty-four playing squares, and only five instead of more than thirty possible moves for the average position. But still tactics and strategies are far from trivial. The total number of possible moves has been estimated at 10^{40}, the digit 1 followed by forty zeros, a sufficiently rich variety to keep the game interesting.

One way of programming a computer to improve its checker game may be indicated by the following example. Suppose you tell the machine to examine all possible variations to a depth of three moves, its move and its opponent's reply and its answering move. That means it analyzes 125 different combinations from a given starting position. (The same depth in chess requires the analysis of 32,768 combinations.) Then it evaluates or "scores" each of the combinations and selects the best of the group to determine its move. But even more important, it remembers the original position and the best combination for that position. Now when the machine is confronted with the same position in a later game, it no longer has to go through its previous analysis all over again. The result of the analysis is stored in its memory unit and can be consulted in a fraction of a second.

Another scene from the CBS television show "The Thinking Machine." Arthur Samuel (standing), IBM investigator of machines that learn, watches a checker game between a human player and an electronic player—a large computer. The computer is about to win this game and type out: "Sorry, you lose."

The machine does not stop there, however. Having already examined the position to a depth of three moves, it goes further and explores three moves deeper and stores the new information which is good for a total depth of six. If it comes across the same position a third time, it already has a six-deep knowledge and probes still another three moves deeper. In other words, it acquires a greater and greater store of knowledge every time it sees a particular position again—until it probes to a maximum depth of twenty moves. After that, it knows the position "cold" and presses on along a known chain of moves.

The machine gains some experiences by playing human opponents. But mostly it learns by playing itself, often by following "book" games which illustrate standard tactics and exceptional combinations. It is also being fed information from about five hundred championship games and variations. The more it plays, of course, the more positions it remembers for reference and deeper analysis in future games. You can see why one major problem is storage capacity. At present the program has built up a memory tape containing nearly 55,000 different positions, and although there is still plenty of room for more information, a time would come when so much information has accumulated that it would take too long to look up a given position.

So Samuel has devised a method for weeding out information. Each position has a sort of "birth certificate" which indicates its age, that is, how long it has been held in memory. About once every twenty moves throughout its playing career the machine adds one unit to the ages of all its stored positions. When a particular position reaches a certain maximum age it is promptly discarded, erased utterly from memory. If this were the only procedure, every position would eventually be erased. But the machine avoids this by a counterpolicy. Every time a position is referred to, the machine arbitrarily divides its age by 2—which, in effect, keeps it young and may indefinitely delay its being discarded.

A similar approach might be followed in libraries. It is as if librarians decided to prevent shelves from becoming jammed by keeping tabs on how often books were called for, and getting rid of all books not used during a sufficiently long period. The approach might work as well for libraries as it does for electronic checkers. Samuel comments: "Now board positions which remain unused are soon forgotten, while board positions which are used several times in succession will be refreshed to such an extent that they will be remembered even if not used thereafter for a fairly long period of time. This form of refreshing and forgetting was adopted on the basis of reflections as to the frailty of human memories. It has proved to be very effective."

The New York investigator has also worked on another learning scheme which requires far less storage space. This method permits a continuing, discard-as-you-go process. After looking ahead a certain number of moves, the machine follows the routine of scoring examined positions on the basis of certain criteria such as back-row control, center control, forced exchanges, and so on. But it also keeps track of the success of its resulting moves and tries to improve its performance by altering the criteria. In other words, it experiments as it plays—increasing or decreasing the relative importance of different criteria and selecting new criteria so that its game becomes stronger and stronger.

To speed the rate of improvement by this method, the machine can be programmed to take the roles of two players, Alpha and Beta. Alpha varies its criteria, while Beta sticks to one set of criteria. If Alpha loses, it has a chance to try again in the next game along the same lines. If Alpha wins, then Beta is given Alpha's current position-evaluation policy and play proceeds. All this, of course, takes place automatically in the computer, which in effect teaches itself during the course of many self-play games.

The checker-playing program has been developed chiefly on a 704 computer, the same type which Bernstein used for his chess program. The machine has a strong psychological edge to start with, enjoying the same sort of advantage as would any cold-blooded, poker-faced human player. Right or wrong, it goes straight through its calculations and moves accordingly. People often find it somewhat disconcerting to deal with an adversary that shows no signs of intellectual effort or doubt. They hesitate, frown, change their minds—and are accustomed to playing against opponents exhibiting similar symptoms.

Another point, which also contributes to the mental hazard of opposing electronic devices, is that the machine moves swiftly. It often makes a move in fifteen seconds and never takes more than thirty seconds. So the machine is idle an appreciable proportion of the time, because its opponents cannot analyze positions and make decisions at that rate. They generally require two minutes or more to figure out what they consider an adequate reply. To keep the machine occupied, to fill in the dead time between the sluggish moves of human players, things may be arranged so that it is pitted against half a dozen different opponents at once.

One game indicates the high quality of the machine's program. The opponent was Edward Lasker, who is always ready and willing to take his chances against all electronic comers—and has described his encounter with the 704: "I play checkers worse than chess, but I felt I could easily see three moves ahead. . . . In the early middle game, out of a clear sky, the computer sacrificed one man, and then two more. I was just about to make a polite remark to Dr. Samuel about the machine's deplorable oversight, when I noticed to my horror that no matter what I played . . . the machine would win back the three men with the better game." Lasker finally won after a tough struggle, but he still recalls that "the machine nearly beat me."

That was back in 1957. The important thing to remember is that Lasker would probably lose to the machine if he played it today. His forte is chess. He is not particularly interested in checkers, and has certainly not bettered his game since his near-loss to the 704. But the machine has been learning slowly and steadily. Furthermore, Samuel has been improving the checker program and is continuing to do so. Following the instructions specified in the program as it now stands, the 704 is capable of playing a good amateur game.

The machine's future is unlimited. Its experience to date consists of several hundred games for a total playing time of perhaps 350 hours. How much more experience would the machine need to attain a master's rating? According to one estimate, a human checkers master has probably played about ten thousand hours. Since the machine plays and learns faster, it might require less than half that time to achieve at least an equivalent status. To stay on the conservative side, we can say that after about five thousand hours of further practice on the Samuel program a 704 computer would be playing master checkers. (The time would be considerably less, of course, with any one of a number of faster machines.)

The only catch to this line of reasoning is the availability and cost of the machine's time. Five thousand hours at about $600 an hour comes to a formidable $3,000,000. But from the standpoint of pure research, the basic problem is already solved. If anyone wanted to put up that amount of money, the machine would be playing tournament-level games within a year. In other words, there is no technical reason why it could not beat the world's best human checker player. Even without the support of a scientifically minded millionaire, this possibility is likely to be realized sooner or later.

Chess presents a far more difficult problem, but by no means an unsolvable problem. In 1958 a reporter asked Mikhail Botvinnik of the Soviet Union, at that time the world's champion, what he thought about the prospects of robot chess: "It seems to me that in the future the machine should surpass the grandmaster. Evidently then, two world championships will take place: one among grandmasters; one among machines." Herbert Simon believes "that within ten years a digital computer will be the world's chess champion, unless the rules bar it from competition." When that happens you can imagine the newspaper stories and editorials, and you can think up your own headlines right now.

In any case, you can see why the old debates about whether or not machines think sound somewhat dated and academic today. We have passed beyond that point. The problem is not whether they think, but how well they think and how their thinking differs from ours. In asking such questions, we are at the frontiers of research on artificial intelligence. We have come to a stage in our discussion where we must consider the nature of human intelligence —and the inconceivably complex workings of the human brain.

THE SHAPING OF THE BRAIN

W<small>E</small> <small>KNOW TO THE LAST DETAIL,</small> to the last wired connection and transistor, the structures of past and present computers. They are of our own making. Files of engineering blueprints specify the nature of their circuits. We understand how they work, and we can repair them readily when they break down. We know considerably less about the design of brains, past and present. The only blueprints we have of these superb, enormously elaborate machines are incomplete. There is considerable research to be done, even though we have learned a great deal during the past three decades. The history of electronic computers is a matter of about twenty years. The history of brains began nearly half a billion years ago.

Brains, like computers, developed because living things were getting more and more complicated. Specifically, they developed to solve problems of communications. A single-celled creature can get along in the world with relatively simple mechanisms to control its activities. But organisms, communities of many specialized cells, present new orders of complexity. As they become bigger, their central and outer regions move farther and farther apart, and if the business of living is to proceed efficiently, every part must "know" what the others are doing. There must be methods of transmitting information swiftly across distances which are increasingly large compared to the size of a cell. The nervous system, like the vascular system, arose in response to this necessity.

The forerunner of modern-style nervous systems is believed to have appeared in times when things which looked something like baked apples represented one of the highest forms of life on earth. They were soft, bulbous, and spineless. You can see their descendants today among starfish and periwinkles and seaweed, reddish-brown sea anemones clinging to rocks in pools along seacoasts. These creatures stay put. The tides bring food to them, and they take what comes through extended tentacles which serve the same purpose as soda straws. Touch the body of a sea anemone anywhere, and it contracts all over. Its nervous system is spread out evenly, forming a diffuse net of fibers.

The first net was extremely crude, but resembled all subsequent nervous systems in one significant respect. It was made up of specialized cells with long, slender fibers. Like roots in a thickly planted garden, the fibers of different cells made contacts with one another. Each cell was a kind of self-charging storage battery designed to produce signals, electrical pulses lasting about a thousandth of a second, the dots and dashes of a natural Morse code. Each cell received signals from, and transmitted signals of its own to, other cells. Nature has used the same basic units, the same sort of connections, and codes based on the same sort of pulses ever since. But the organization of the units, the circuitry of the nervous system, has changed radically.

New designs came with creatures more advanced than the rock-clingers, things on the go, explorers and hunters and killers. They developed solid, backboned, streamlined bodies—fore-and-aft structures—for cutting through the water in search of food—and for closing in on prey and escaping from predators. The front or prow end of the organism became more and more important. This was the nosey, butting-in part which meets the world head-on and usually gets into trouble first. It developed as a control center to coordinate actions considerably more varied than the mass over-all contractions of sea anemones.

In swimmers the loose net underwent a complete transformation. It became a compact, elongated structure. The spinal cord, a bundle of many fibers, ran the length of the body like a great superhighway connected, through subsidiary control centers, with outlying regions by branching roads and lanes and dead-end alleys. The fibers led to the head end, where many cells clustered into densely packed nerve centers. Nature had arrived at a design which would be altered in many ways, but would still retain the same fundamental organization—a cable composed of signal-carrying fibers running to a central control station up front, a brain.

Imagine a time-lapse motion picture showing as a continuous, speeded-up process what has happened since then. Each frame of the film represents millennia of development. You see the brain growing and unfolding and folding back upon itself like a strange tropical flower. Bulges at the very top of the head end of the spinal cord become larger, and a barely discernible change begins to take place some 300 million years ago—another innovation. It comes not long after life dragged itself out of the seas, after fish with lungs or the precursors of lungs crawled over stretches of dry land and managed to survive in suffocating air. It is a sign that nature is conducting new experiments among creatures that can live on land as well as in water.

The change first appears on the bulge farthest up front, the forebrain. You see a gray patch smaller than the nail on your little finger. The patch spreads across the surface as if it were a parasitic growth. Now it is a moving sheet which flows down over the curving front of the forebrain and curls underneath like a ram's horn. It creeps down into the very bottoms of clefts and grooves in the surface and climbs up the other sides, filling every nook and cranny and forming an intricate system of rolls and convolutions. At the end of the motion picture, after ages of evolution, it dominates the entire scene and buries older structures completely. This cerebral cortex or "outer bark," the highest center of all, has reached a high stage of development in man.

The human brain may be regarded as the headquarters of a far-flung communications network. In other words, its job is to deal with information. It is a place for the analysis of data and the making of decisions. Its many centers work together in an effort to make sense of things, to anticipate events and solve problems. It never has a chance for complete rest, because problems are always with us. They arise continually in a world which is always changing and often confusing. They multiply almost like living things, and no sooner have we solved one problem than new and more difficult problems arise to plague or challenge us. We are adjusted to the world for brief periods only.

But the brain does its best to keep us on an even keel, to steer us with as few mishaps as possible toward our goals and destinations. Its nerve pathways are wires of a sort, living conductors of electricity, fibers insulated by fatty sheaths. They form a maze of channels connecting different parts of the brain with one another—and connecting the entire brain complex with the remotest parts of the body. They are routes along which signals flash in a continual relay race, passing step by step from one nerve cell to the next in the patterns of cerebral circuits.

The word "signal" is no figure of speech. The electrical pulses of the nervous system are signals in the most literal sense, and help us distinguish the quality of sensation.

When you put your hands in lukewarm water, certain nerve cells embedded in your skin respond by firing or emitting pulses at a regular rate determined by the temperature of the water. As the water gets hotter, the firing rate increases proportionately. If the rate were, say, seventy pulses a second for relatively low temperatures, it might rise to several hundred pulses a second at high temperatures. Built-in thermometers register temperatures and translate the temperatures into series of electrical "beats."

Other sense organs deal with intensities in the same way. We respond to wide ranges of sensation: from a delicate touch on the skin to heavy pressure, from a faint rustle of leaves to the crashing of cymbals, from the faintest glimmer of light in a dark room to the glare of the sun at high noon. Coded pulses help us keep track of events, maintain our bearings in the world outside us. Also, we automatically keep track of and adjust to the demands of the inner world of our bodies. We have more than 200 pairs of muscles, and every one of them contains detectors which measure degrees of tension by producing characteristic pulse frequencies in appropriate nerves. The levels of sugar in the blood, blood pressure and heart action, the intensity of hunger and thirst and desires—all these things are similarly measured.

In other words, our sense organs function as meters. Imagine a telegraph operator at a railroad station watching an approaching express train, with his finger on a transmitting key. The nearer the train comes and the louder the sound of the locomotive, the faster he operates the key and the higher the frequency of telegraphic pulses. The frequency reaches a peak when the train is passing the station, and slows down as it recedes. This is a rough analogy to the automatic workings of some sense organs. Actual nerve frequencies may vary from a few pulses a second to more than 1,000, although they generally fall in the 50-to-200 range. These pulses are codes, codes by which information is fed into the circuits of the nervous system.

So signals of many sorts flash from the toes upward, through special nerve fibers for each sense. Like the tributaries of a great river, they converge on the central channel of the spinal cord. They join the mass flow of signals ascending toward the oversized bulge at the top of the cord, the brain. A large number of signals go all the way, reaching the summit and entering the cortex. Fibers carrying different kinds of information, coded impulses which represent different senses, run to different areas of the cortex.

For example, suppose you see a man's face some 6 feet away. It forms an image about the size of a pinhead on the retina of the eye, a mosaic sheet made up of cells which resemble the grains of a photographic film in that they change chemically when light falls on them. The chemical changes produce electrical pulses in a flexible cable of a million fibers which is known as the optic nerve and runs to the cortex. More specifically, the fibers run to a particular part of the cortex, the visual area at the back of the brain—and different sections of this map represent different sections of the retina. Thus, a representation of the man's face corresponding to the retina image is plotted part for part on the surface of the brain.

There is another feature of the visual map. Optic-nerve fibers spread out like raveled ends from a cable so that they form an enlarged map on the cortex. After all, if the image were as small on the cortex as on the retina, you would not be able to see anything in fine detail. When you look closely at part of a face or when you read, tiny retinal images may be "magnified" as much as several thousand times on the visual map. Other maps are reduced in scale. Sensations from different parts of the skin, which has a total area of about 20 square feet, are plotted on a section of cortex about as large as a book of matches.

The "sound" map, a strip at the side of the brain, is a kind of anatomical keyboard. Signals representing low notes flow along fibers running to one end of the strip, high-note signals enter the other end, and intermediate-note signals enter at corresponding sites in between. There are special maps for smell, taste, and other sensations, as well as sight and hearing. The cortex can be thought of as a center including a set of active or "flickering" charts. Pulses relayed from sense organs form changing patterns on the charts, changing electrical displays which indicate the state of activity in remote parts of the body and in even more remote parts of the outside world.

These signals are the brain's input. They are sorted in the cortex, routed to their appropriate mapping areas. Then the brain analyzes the information, recombines some of it into new patterns, and makes decisions. We do not know much about the detailed workings of these processes, which will be considered in the next chapter, but the results are solutions to the various problems confronting us. The brain produces solutions in a continual stream, because the flow of problems is also continual. The answers take the form of outgoing signals, patterns of pulses coded in a way similar to those of signals coming in from sense organs. These messages flow downstream from the brain along descending fibers of the spinal cord, fibers which branch out from the cord at different points and make contact with muscles.

The muscles respond in various ways. The messages may represent orders to do certain things, and we move accordingly—in patterns determined by patterns of nerve pulses which represent the brain's instructions. Or we may do nothing. Instructions from the highest centers may inhibit instead of stimulating our muscles. The strategy of living calls for timing, for delays as well as immediate responses. We may decide never to act or form elaborate plans for future action. In any case, all such behavior is the result of signals flashed in code from brain to muscles. We do things or avoid doing them on the basis of cerebral messages.

Considerable research has been required to discover even the most elementary facts about the brain. Look at a piece of nerve tissue under the microscope and all you see is apparent chaos, a tangle of cell bodies and fibers so confusing that a great investigator of the past called it "the cerebral jungle." But there are paths and meeting places and terminals and circuits in this jungle. The brain is the most highly organized organ of the body. Indeed, it is the most highly organized and complex system that we know about anywhere in the universe. One clue to its fundamental structure and workings comes from studies of how it takes shape during the growth of the embryo.

The basic process is the development of a full-grown adult from a barely visible speck of living matter, a fertilized human ovum. Every step of this intricate process occurs according to a marvelously precise timetable. During the earliest stages of development the original egg multiplies many times, but individual cells are not yet committed. That is, they have not yet specialized into muscles, bone, and other tissues. Changes come soon enough, however. For example, at various stages uncommitted cells in different regions of the *ectoderm*, or outer layer of the embryo, become hair, nails, sweat glands, skin, the lens of the eye, tooth enamel, and so on.

The nervous system also develops from the ectoderm. A sheet of tissue begins creeping across part of the inner side of this layer, and wherever the moving front of the sheet touches ectoderm cells they are transformed into nerve cells. Your nervous system started forming 8½ months before you were born, when you were about a twenty-fifth of an inch tall. But the term "nerve cell" is an extremely broad one. There are many kinds of nerve cells, which means that descendants of the original population must specialize a great deal more along many different lines.

They must play a variety of different roles in the spinal cord, optic nerve, and retina, and in the centers of the brain. Whatever mechanism determines the nature of embryological development, and the sequences of steps involved, a large part of it must be devoted to the formation of the nervous system. The human body contains about two hundred different types of cells, and more than half of them are nerve cells.

The brain, like the rest of the body, is built to specifications originally set down in hereditary blueprints. Thirty years ago we knew practically nothing about the design of these blueprints, about nature's method of transmitting inherited patterns from generation to generation—and controlling the structure of living tissue. Today we are beginning to understand the process. The key discovery came from a British investigator, Francis Crick, working together with an American colleague, James Watson, at Cambridge University in England. In about a month of intensive study they added new insights of their own to the findings of others and constructed the first plausible model of the substance of heredity, the stuff out of which genes are made.

The substance is referred to as DNA (short for deoxyribonucleic acid). According to the Crick-Watson model, its molecule consists of two chains of atoms wound together in a double helix, a kind of spiral-staircase formation. The entire structure is built out of six fundamental units, sugar and phosphate and four chemical groups known as "bases"—generally adenine, guanine, thymine, and cytosine. DNA molecules are giants, among the largest known. They may contain large numbers of each of the building blocks, but there are only six different blocks in every case.

This is perhaps the most striking discovery in the history

of modern biology. It tells us that living things, for all their enormous diversity, are amazingly similar when it comes to their submicroscopic structure. Bacteria which survive in the steaming waters of hot springs, polyps building coral reefs and islands, deep-sea fish with eyes on stalks and round glowing lights like portholes along their sides, meat-eating plants and mammoth redwood trees, snakes and giraffes and tigers and man with his swollen brain—the forms of these and all other creatures are determined by genes they receive from their parents. The earth houses some 2 million species, and every one of them is what it is because of its inherited DNA molecules.

The DNA of every species consists of six essential units. Furthermore, the units always seem to be arranged in the same spiral-staircase structure. The sugar and phosphate units are always linked together alternately to form long strands. The four bases are always attached to the strands like clusters of grapes to vines. In view of such similarities among DNA molecules or genes, how is it that species may differ so widely from one another? Crick and Watson answered this question by assuming that the secret lies in the order of the bases strung out along the sugar-phosphate strands.

Imagine that the spiral DNA molecules of a certain species were untwisted and stretched taut into a single chain. The four bases—we shall abbreviate them as A, G, T, and C—are arranged in a long series along the chain. Now in theory, if we knew the exact arrangement for every type of DNA, we could tell what species this series represented. All we would have to do is read off the sequence of bases like information on a ticker tape. Thus, the sequence A-C-T-G . . . G-A-T-C might represent a scarlet-fever germ, G-T-A-A . . . T-C-G-A a mouse, and C-A-G-G . . . A-T-C-G a man.

Notice what this theory implies. For one thing, there are

some 2 million types of DNA, one for each species. Relatively large differences in the base sequences of these types determine the differences among species, the way they behave, and the nervous systems which control their behavior. Furthermore, smaller differences in patterns of the four bases determine the differences among strains or breeds within a given species—and still smaller differences account for the fact that no two individuals are exactly alike (except for identical twins). You differ from other people, because the DNA molecules you inherited from your parents differ slightly from the DNA molecules they inherited. The precise order in which the bases are arranged is extremely important.

In a fundamental sense, we are speaking of nothing less than codes. The base sequence in human DNA represents a message, a message from past generations which directs the shaping of generations to come. It concerns the process of growth from embryo to adult, spelling out plans for the synthesis of thousands of special proteins and other substances required to form cells and tissues. It also spells out the entire manufacturing schedule: the order in which the substances shall be synthesized, how much of each, and at what rates. This is automation at the molecular level.

The DNA message may be thought of as a very long telegram whose words are made up of various combinations of the four bases, A and G and C and T. The telegram has a great deal to say. Human DNA contains an estimated 20 billion bases, and if the information they represent were printed out in full, it would fill about three hundred volumes each as large as the big dictionaries found in reference libraries. This is necessary information. It includes the complete description for the making of a human being. Nature has compressed it all into highly coiled molecules packed tight in the nuclei of cells. It is a list of coded instructions to be followed in a definite order.

The language of heredity is written in an alphabet of only four letters.

Our inherited messages must be duplicated accurately as they are passed from generation to generation, from parents to children, from every dividing cell to the two resulting cells. As a matter of fact, mistakes are rare. A message is generally copied several million times (that is, DNA molecules duplicate themselves several million times) before an error crops up. But that is often enough to cause trouble. Misprints and errata are mutations, sports and freaks and hereditary weaknesses of all sorts. The deviation may be exceedingly small, a few misplaced or missing bases in a molecule containing many millions of bases. Yet the outcome may be faulty workmanship, a flaw in the building of a vital part of the body, a susceptibility to disease or constitutional weakness. A defect in the brain may express itself as nervousness or neurosis or major mental illness.

Errors or no errors, the embryo proceeds strictly and automatically according to the rules of the game. It obeys its instructions in a systematic manner, and blindly, whether or not they make complete sense. In other words it obeys a program "written out" along the coiled strands of DNA molecules. The program's patterns of chemical bases may be compared to patterns of holes or magnetic spots on paper tapes fed into electronic computers.

The brain, like the rest of the body, is shaped by this program and these patterns. Its growth follows a genetically determined schedule. For example, some nerve fibers do not work at peak efficiency until they are covered with insulating sheaths, and among the first fibers to develop such sheaths are certain reflex-controlling nerves in the spinal cord. This usually takes place around the end of the fourth month after fertilization, when the fetus is about 6½ inches long. By the sixth fetal month the process occurs in a bundle of fibers which runs from the ear to the cord and is concerned with balance and equilibrium. A month or so later sheathing forms on fibers involved in the smoothing and coordination of automatic movements. The entire brain and nervous system develops in a step-by-step fashion before birth—and after.

At birth the brain may weigh 11 or 12 ounces, or about the weight of an adult chimpanzee's brain. It will weigh some 3 pounds before it stops growing, and most of that increase takes place in the cortex and its associated nerve fibers. The sheathing of important fibers carrying executive messages from the cortex does not take place on a large scale until after birth. Furthermore, it proceeds from the head downward; that is, the shortest pathways tend to be completely insulated first. Thus, an infant begins to control its eye movements before it controls the movements of its arms, hands, and legs in that order. Insulation of cortex-to-spine nerve bundles is most rapid during the end of the first year of life and the early part of the second year, when the infant is acquiring the control that leads to walking.

Walking is one of the many abilities which come at their scheduled time and are retained for a lifetime. But our genetic programs may call for the disappearance as well as the appearance of abilities; nerve channels may be blocked or shut off as well as opened. For example, we are born with the so-called "grasp reflex." An infant will curl its fingers tightly around a stick and keep its grip with an impressive persistence. A case is on record of a three-week-old baby clinging to a bar with one hand and holding itself suspended for more than 2½ minutes, which is something few adults can do. The grasp reflex is established by an ancient part of the DNA program, by genes probably passed on from times when man's remote ancestors lived in trees and a tenacious grip was more important than it is now. In us, the reflex vanishes within a few months after birth.

Animal studies reveal further details about circuits built into the nervous system according to inherited codes. Such circuits are involved in much of the automatic behavior which we call instinct, and an M.I.T. research group has reported new findings concerning their structure. Jerome Lettvin, Humberto Maturana, Warren McCulloch, and Walter Pitts, of the Research Laboratory of Electronics, inserted very fine needlelike contacts or microelectrodes into fibers of the frog's optic nerve—picking up electrical signals in individual fibers as the frog watched events taking place around it. They found that the nerve, a cable of some half a million fibers, is a complex and highly organized detecting system.

Fibers are specialized so that they produce signals only in response to specific varieties of visual pattern. One type of fiber responds best when the frog sees a small dark object entering its field of vision, stopping, and then moving about intermittently. Such fibers are, in effect, "bug perceivers." The optic nerve includes three other types of fiber which detect sharply defined edges in a small area of the visual field, or changes of distribution of light within a larger area, or average dimming of light in the largest area. The four kinds of fibers become four sheets of nerve endings in the brain. Each of the sheets maps the retina and, when the optic nerve is severed, the fibers grow back and re-establish working connections, reconstituting the four sheets and the map.

This precise circuitry reflects the almost robotlike nature of many of the animal's essential activities, a point emphasized by the Cambridge workers: "The frog does not seem to see or, at any rate, is not concerned with the detail of stationary parts of the world around him. He will starve to death surrounded by food if it is not moving. His choice of food is determined only by size and movement. He will leap to capture any object the size of an insect or worm, providing it moves like one. He can be fooled easily not only by a bit of dangled meat but by any moving small object. His sex life is conducted by sound and touch. His choice of paths in escaping enemies does not seem to be governed by anything more devious than leaping to where it is darker."

Automatic behavior implying built-in nervous circuitry is also typical of creatures which are more advanced than frogs. It has been observed, for example, that ducklings scuttle about in alarm at the sight of a wooden cross passing overhead, short end first. Yet if you fly the cross in reverse, long end first, the ducklings pay no attention. In a recent study, Ronald Melzack of M.I.T. has shown that these fear reactions occur in ducklings raised in complete isolation at their first sight of the wooden cross.

One explanation is that for ages the destroyers of ducks have included birds like hawks with short necks and long tails, so ducklings have evolved with a built-in fear for such things. To them the cross flown short end first represented a kind of "artificial hawk." But ducklings generally have nothing to fear from their own kind, things with long necks and short tails. The cross flown long end first produced no reaction. Ducklings are born with nerve structures for distinguishing friend from foe.

The Austrian naturalist Konrad Lorenz, a pioneer in the study of animal behavior, has a great deal to say about birds in general and ducklings in particular. He notes that mallard ducklings react instinctively to a characteristic duck call, which he writes out as "quahg, gegegegeg," following the sound whatever its source: "Anything that emits the right quack will be considered as mother, whether it is a fat white Pekin duck or a still fatter man." Lorenz has spent hours emitting the right quack and leading doting

Ronald Melzack of M.I.T., with duckling and experimental apparatus. Long, turning metal arm attached to top of tripod . . .

broods of ducklings. He found it a trying task. Mother mallards quack incessantly, and the young birds became worried and panicky if he stopped for even a short time.

This line of research has been extended at the University of Chicago and other institutions. One finding is that ducklings are "ripe" for reacting to the mother-call at a sharply defined period—about thirteen to sixteen hours after hatching. If they hear the quacking at that age, even if it comes from a tape recording and a male decoy, they will follow it for the rest of their young lives. But before or after the so-called "imprinting" period, the reaction is considerably less effective and the result may be maladjusted mallards in later life. The indication is strong that the brain is not only constructed according to hereditary

pulls cut-out silhouette through the air above duckling. If the silhouette moves stub-nosed end first, resembling profile of hawk or other potential enemy, duckling shows alarm. If it moves long-neck end first, the profile resembles that of a goose or duck and the duckling is unconcerned.

DNA blueprints, but that there is a definite building schedule. Furthermore, particular nervous mechanisms are designed to be used at particular times; otherwise the animal may not develop normally.

The scheduled ripening of nerve centers continues into later life. A remarkable example occurs among certain birds raised in captivity. They may be brought up in completely unnatural environments, in cages and living rooms, isolated from other birds. They see no trees, leaves, twigs, bushes. But at the right time, as precisely as if there were some sort of innate countdown, they proceed to act out a strange pantomime—going through all the motions of building nests, and bedding the nests down for eggs and offspring that will never be produced.

Such behavior is as close to being 100 per cent automatic as anything we know of. A duckling reacting to its first hawk, real or simulated, also behaves according to inherited patterns. But that depends on seeing something, an appropriate stimulus from the environment. The point about the nest-building reaction is that no external stimulus or signal is required, no mate appears and there are no seasons in living rooms. Independently of events in the outer world, the brain somehow triggers itself—turns itself on like an electric range or a clock radio.

This is how nature designs living things for their futures. All existing organisms are the result of millions of years of natural selection, the latest models created by an ancient trial-and-error process. In times past, some of the ancestors of contemporary ducklings saved their lives by reacting promptly and at an early age to visual signals representing "hawk!" Other ancestors equipped with less efficient early warning systems, the carriers of less useful genes, died more frequently and were ultimately weeded out. Of course, hawks evolved too and became more expert at killing. Evolution, like warfare, demands a continual development of competing offensive and defensive mechanisms.

The same sorts of responses are found throughout the range of life, to the very top of the evolutionary ladder. We are products of the same trial-and-error process. Human infants are not deprived of their mothers to study the nature of their built-in cerebral patterns, but there is no reason to believe that their behavior would differ basically from the behavior of experimentally orphaned ducklings. If monkey experiments are any clue, human infants might be expected to respond to warmth and softness rather than to sound in forming their mother-associations. According to one speculation, the ability to perform such automatic reactions efficiently should start declining at the age of five to six months, which is about the time when infants begin to be afraid of things.

We know that what happens during infancy and early childhood may play an important part in determining the way we behave later. The psychoanalyst speaks of the id and ego and superego, Oedipus and castration complexes, hostilities and repressions. To the brain investigator striving to deal with and discover elements more susceptible to experimental study, "ripeness is all." Our emotional behavior may be understood by studying the maturing nervous system, the inherited codes which shape it, and the biological clocks which time the shaping process.

Similar factors seem to be involved in intellectual as well as emotional development. The Swiss psychologist Jean Piaget has found that our ability to think logically comes step by step in a definite sequence. For example, take the concept of number. A child can learn the names of numbers at an early age and count, say, ten blocks in a row. But if you arrange the blocks in more elaborate patterns or pile them up, he may become confused. The full notion of number, the realization that "ten" is something independent of how the blocks are arranged and is a common feature of ten red blocks and ten blue blocks, does not generally come until about the age of 6½ or 7. The idea that objects of different sizes and shapes may weigh the same usually comes between eleven and twelve, and it takes another year or so before a child realizes that differently shaped objects may occupy the same volume.

Development continues into later life. Our brains and nervous systems do not complete their growth until we are in our twenties. After that we gain in experience, although there is evidence that our ability to grasp and adjust to new ideas begins declining appreciably between thirty and thirty-five. This brings us to one of the most striking features of the brain. When muscle and nerve and bone and skin cells die, the body manufactures new cells to take their places. But brain cells are not replaced. You are born with all you will ever have, some 10 billion; when a brain cell dies, it is gone forever and never replaced.

Think of what this means in terms of normal aging processes. That fixed supply is dwindling at an accelerating rate. It has been estimated that a person loses an average of 30,000 brain cells every day of his life. Yet we may retain some of our most valuable mental faculties as we grow older, because among the brain's built-in mechanisms is a kind of insurance system or safety factor. The tangled feltwork of the brain includes so many connections that the disappearance of millions of pathways, the loss of millions of cells, may produce relatively little effect. More often than not there are alternative pathways, other routes to carry the flow of important signals.

So a considerable body of recent research suggests that a great deal of our activity throughout life has an automatic quality. We behave like human beings because we are constructed that way. In us, as in creatures lower on the scale of evolution, the general design of the brain is precoded. The design is determined by specifications written in the four-letter alphabet of DNA molecules. We have a great deal to learn about the degree of detail specified beforehand in our genes, and what we learn may surprise us.

A leading investigator in this area, Roger Sperry of the California Institute of Technology, summarizes the views of many of his colleagues: "Almost no behavior pattern need be considered too refined or too complicated for its detailed organization to be significantly influenced by genetic factors. The extent to which our individual motor skills, sensory capacities, talents, temperaments, mannerisms, intelligence and other behavioral traits may be products of inheritance would seem to be much greater . . . than many of us had formerly believed possible."

CHAPTER 10

THE MIND IN ACTION

DUGESIA TIGRINA is a cross-eyed flatworm half an inch to an inch long and about as wide as a paper match. It is most at home in dark places which it finds by the simple process of moving away from light. Put it in a T-shaped maze with one branch leading to a dark and the other to a brightly lit box, and after a sufficient number of trials it can be conditioned to turn in the right direction. Furthermore, if you cut a conditioned flatworm in half, the head end will grow a new tail and the tail end will grow a new head—and the two new flatworms, the "tail end" as well as the "head end" creature, will remember a significant part of what the severed flatworm had learned.

The flatworm occupies a humble position in the hierarchy of living things. Its brain, the most primitive known, contains only a few thousand nerve cells and is smaller than the head of a pin. But that is sufficient to permit a degree of learning. *Dugesia* is of special interest to brain investigators, because it illustrates a basic point about organisms from the simplest to the most complex. At every level we find built-in activity, instincts determined by precoded hereditary information spelled out in genes or DNA molecules. At every level we find ample evidence of nervous circuits as precisely constructed as if they had been manufactured according to detailed wiring diagrams. And at every level we find behavior as rigid and stereotyped as that of the bird which goes through the motions of nest-building when it has been reared from birth in a living-room cage.

Yet, for all such automatic features, we know there is something else. All brains may be shaped by experience as well as heredity, which is merely another way of saying that they have flexible features. They include uncommitted nerve cells and pathways, connections that have not been predetermined once and for all—and can be established and modified and broken in the light of newly acquired knowledge. This capacity is most highly developed in the human brain. Experiments do not reveal what proportion of its circuitry is uncommitted, set aside for learning, or how that proportion compares with similar circuitry in lower brains. But it is enough to make an enormous difference.

We are, above all, learners. We cannot help learning, and certain studies of our unique capacity for neurosis indicate that we may suffer from not learning. We discard superstitions, theories that have outlived their purposes, outmoded ways of doing things. From toilet training on, we learn to control and modify built-in behavior. We go on reducing diets and hunger strikes, practice celibacy, and train ourselves to control at will such reflexes as the rate of our heartbeats or the contraction and dilation of the eyes' pupils.

We evolve primarily by learning, which is something new under the sun. Other animals can exist in harmony with their surroundings just as their ancestors did millions or tens of millions of years ago. We are forever restless and create as well as solve problems. We have advanced from rock shelters and caves to skyscrapers, from flints to bulldozers, from finger counting to computers. Yet the structure of our brains has not changed. People with brains like ours first appeared on earth at least 50,000 years ago and perhaps a long time before that. Everything we have accomplished is the result of exploiting the most flexible parts of the brain, the centers in which new nerve pathways may be established by experience. They represent our capacity to deal with the future, to get along with one another, and to undertake increasingly ambitious explorations of the universe.

When it comes to the workings of these centers, however, we are still largely in the dark. To account for the highest functions of the human brain, we have speculations rather than well-tested evidence. For example, if we understood how the brain stores its remembrances of things past, the way would be clear for an intensive analysis of learning and imagination and discovery. But the problem of memory has not yet been solved, and remains as perhaps the greatest current challenge to research workers.

Indeed, the problem has been playing a game of hare and hounds with us for a long while now. From time to time in the past research groups have announced that they had at last "cornered" memory, that it was situated in this or that part of the brain. Such announcements are rarer today. Many investigators feel that searching for *the* seat of memory is a will-o'-the-wisp effort. There may be no such thing. Our memory traces seem to be stored in many places, and perhaps each trace is duplicated many times so that if one location is destroyed, records may endure elsewhere. In any event, several important centers are apparently involved in the workings of our complex storage systems.

A strategically placed decision-making center, the so-called "reticular (netlike) formation," provides a case in point. This gray column of tightly packed cells is found in the brainstem, the bulging extension of the spinal cord into the skull. It lies just to one side of the nerve-fiber cables carrying signals from many sense organs, and side branches from the cables feed into it. The signals make a continual hubbub. Each one of them can be thought of as a sort of shout coming from a place where something requires readjusting and is relaying its electrical protests upstream toward executive headquarters.

The brain is subjected to a continual barrage of such demands for attention. They must be recognized and silenced, or else we should have no peace. Yet it is impossible to handle them all at the top levels, for they are legion. Every single second of your waking life millions of electrical pulses flow from sense organs into your nervous system. If the whole lot reached the highest centers of your brain, there would be a chaotic traffic jam of information. You would soon go mad. As a matter of fact, some major mental illnesses may result when regulating mechanisms break down and too many messages burst in upon the highest centers like floodwaters after the collapse of a dam.

The reticular formation is one of the structures designed to protect us against such disasters. More specifically, it is a kind of sorting place analogous to the waiting room outside the offices of the head of a great industrial empire— where a staff of secretaries know the boss's schedule for the day and what is important to him and who, among all the incoming visitors, should be let into the inner sanctum or directed to lesser executives. The brainstem center is in two-way communication with the top "executive" of the cerebral organization, the cortex, which is reserved for high-priority matters only. So the reticular formation keeps the flow of messages to the cortex within bounds, cuts the flow to a minimum when we turn in for the night, and helps rouse us next morning.

And it either contains some of our memory files or else has rapid access to them. Recent studies indicate that among the many patterns of nerve impulses entering its intricate pathways, it can select those which represent something new. It presumably does this by some sort of matching process, comparing the incoming patterns with stored patterns. If there is no match, if the storehouses of past experience contain no records of a new pattern, the reticular formation relays it upstairs to the cortex together with a "startle" or arousal signal which is roughly the equivalent of a memo marked URGENT. The new pattern is stored for future reference; when it loses its novelty, it will no longer be passed to the cortex. In other words, it will be filed away and preserved and used again—and so will the appropriate reaction.

Also concerned with memory is a center buried deep near the region between the cerebral hemispheres, a curled-up bit of tissue about 2 inches long and known as the hippocampus. ("Hippocampus" is Latin for "sea horse," but the tissue looks more like a miniature jelly roll.) Patients suffering from damage to this center may be unable to form memories of recent experiences, although they are completely normal when it comes to recalling the past.

One woman moved to a new apartment and could not find her way around in it. Every time she came home, it was like entering a strange place for the first time. She could not, and still cannot, remember the layout of the apartment. Another patient, a railroad engineer, drives his car to and from work every day and performs his regular duties as well as he did before his injury. But he cannot tell you what he had for breakfast.

There is a peculiar gap in the lives of these patients. As far as memory is concerned, they live chiefly in the past, in a past dating before the time of their affliction. They also live fleetingly in a thin slice of the present, a brief fringe period, for they can remember what happened five or ten minutes ago. It is as if current experiences set up memory echoes in the brain, which reverberate and die away leaving no records to show that they once existed. The gap involves a time between the remote past and the immediate present, the recent past. As in old age, something has gone wrong with the mechanisms that produce new memory traces.

Incidentally, the hippocampus itself is part of a system of centers associated with emotion. An injury in this system restricted to an area less than a tenth of an inch across, and located in the proper region, creates what investigators call "angry rabbits." This is a considerable understatement, for the operation has a Jekyll-to-Hyde effect. It transforms a normally timid rabbit into a snapping, snarling animal which goes after investigators and anything else in sight. One chubby white rabbit attacked, and routed, a large dog.

Damage to other centers in this system—produced experimentally in animals and as a result of disease in human beings—may cause intense fear, pleasurable feelings, incessant hunger or thirst, abnormal sexual behavior, and many other bizarre symptoms. But the fact that certain recent-memory mechanisms are included in the same system that involves emotional behavior is something yet to be explained.

Finally we come to the cortex, where, as you might expect, some of the subtlest memory processes take place. Much of what we know about the human cortex was discovered during operations designed to treat brain tumors, epilepsy, and other diseases. Operations of this sort may be performed using a local anesthetic only, to kill pain in the scalp; the brain itself feels no pain. So the patient may be fully conscious, a fact which permits surgeons to make certain important observations before removing tissue.

As a routine procedure, they use an electrical probe or electrode to stimulate and identify certain areas which must be left intact. For example, if the visual map at the back of the brain is stimulated, the patient will report seeing "dancing lights," "colored balls whirling," "radiating gray spots," and so on. Sensations of numbness or tingling help locate the map receiving sensory signals from the skin, while the patient hears buzzing or humming or ringing sounds when his hearing map is stimulated. Dr. Wilder Penfield of the Montreal Neurological Institute, a former All-American football player as well as a leading surgeon and brain investigator, has pioneered in such explorations.

Dr. Penfield is especially interested in the so-called "temporal cortex," the part that covers the sides of the brain and folds inward underneath its base. One of his most dramatic cases was that of D. F., a twenty-six-year-old secretary who was being operated on for an epileptic condition involving her right temporal cortex. The surgeon touched a tiny area of the upper part of the gray sheet with the tip of the electrode—and the patient responded: "I hear music. It is like radio." She began humming the tune, as if she were listening to an orchestra and keeping time with it. Suddenly she stopped humming abruptly. Dr. Penfield had raised the tip of the electrode, breaking the contact.

When he touched the same spot again, the patient hummed the same tune. But she did not pick up the tune from the point where she had stopped a moment before. She began all over again from the beginning—and that happened every time the contact was broken and remade. Instead of continuing, even after an extremely brief interval, she always went back to the very first note. It was as if a submicroscopic reel of sound-recording tape were unwinding in her mind, and then rewinding itself rapidly after each successive playback.

In the last test the electrode was kept in place for about thirty seconds. The patient hummed through the entire tune while, in Dr. Penfield's words, "all in the operating room listened in astonished silence." Then a nurse remarked: "I know it. It's 'Marching Along Together.'"

"Yes, those are the words in it," the patient replied, "but I don't know whether that's the name of the song."

Files at the Montreal Neurological Institute contain records of other cases like that of D. F. And in every case the process of recollection has the same playback feature, a repeating quality which hints at the existence of some sort of mechanical information-retrieval or reference system somewhere in the brain's maze of nerve fibers. Furthermore, stimulating the temporal cortex often produces another interesting phenomenon. We have all had the experience of sitting down in a strange living room or restaurant, sometimes among strangers, and suddenly feeling that the whole setting is familiar. You have been here before, sitting in the same chair and facing in the same direction and with the same people. You feel that you know what is going to happen and what will be said, word for word. Flashbacks and illusions of flashbacks somehow concern the circuitry of the temporal cortex.

Here is how Dr. Penfield summarizes his findings about this part of the cortex: "There is hidden away in the brain a record of the stream of consciousness. It seems to hold the detail of that stream as laid down during each man's waking, conscious hours. Contained in this record are all those things of which the individual was once aware—such details as a man might hope to remember for a few seconds or minutes afterwards, but which are largely lost to voluntary recall after that time. . . . This is not memory, as we usually use the word. No man can recall by voluntary effort such a wealth of detail. . . . Many a patient has told me that the experience brought back by the electrode is much more real than remembering."

All the evidence to date, the evidence we have outlined and a great deal more, emphasizes the elusive and scattered nature of memory. It is not in the reticular formation or the hippocampus. It is not in the temporal cortex. Dr. Penfield believes that the recollections evoked by stimulating this region come from a place or places elsewhere in the brain. He feels that the temporal cortex seems to flash information-please signals to memory, requests for precise information concerning patterns of a particular past. But neither he nor anyone else knows where our archives of times past are stored.

The search continues. Memory is of crucial importance in understanding the most human features of the human brain. We share with other animals the sort of inherited nerve patterns which determine instinctive, automatic behavior. Man's uniqueness as a species depends on his ability to keep adjusting and readjusting, to invent and try new tactics and strategies when old ones get him nowhere, to drop futile activities quickly, to form and modify habits effectively. Underlying all these changes are corresponding changes in the brain, changes in nerve cells produced by the impact and repeated proddings of experience, changes representing records of past successes and failures.

Since the nature of memory remains unknown, no one can provide a scientific measure of its capacity. But estimates, even the most conservative, are quite impressive. Suppose that an elderly gentleman with time on his hands —say, a retired statesman or general—decided to write, not his memoirs, but a list of every single thing stored in his head. The list is to include the names of people he has known or read about, what he remembers of his life and the lives of others, facts concerning his profession, news and history, plays and movies and receptions, and so on and on. (We assume that he has total recall, that he can remember everything.) He sits down and starts typing at a steady pace of 100 words a minute, twenty-four hours a day. How long would it take him to prepare an exhaustive inventory of things stored?

According to one modest estimate, it would take about four months and two weeks. He would write some 200 million words, or, to put it in more mathematical terms, an amount of information which can be coded into a billion binary digits or bits. That is roughly the total information contained in the twenty-four volumes of the *Encyclopaedia Britannica*. More generous estimates credit the brain with a capacity as high as a million times greater, which indicates, among other things, how little investigators actually know and how far they are from anything approaching precision in this matter. But whatever figure you use, it is clear that the files of memory are voluminous.

A major problem right now is to discover in what form memory traces are stored. One theory, and as yet there are nothing but theories, has been inspired by research on heredity. Heredity is passed on from generation to generation in genes, DNA molecules coiled up in eggs and sperms and carrying coded messages of a kind. As pointed out in the last chapter, the messages consist of long chains of four basic chemical units which, like the letters of an alphabet, are arranged in a wide variety of different combinations. In other words, giant molecules carry information concerning the inherited past, the past of the human species.

Perhaps the acquired past, the past of the individual, is recorded in a similar way. Perhaps the brain can translate patterns of electrical pulses, signals representing information from the sense organs, into corresponding patterns of chemical units in giant molecules. If so, here is what might happen when you see a new face. In the first place, you do not have to store every detail. The details which this face has in common with faces previously seen—the general oval shape, the general location and structure and coloring of the features, and so on—are already recorded. For example, patterns of nerve signals representing "oval" have left their marks on molecules already existing in various brain cells. You remember unique things only, out-of-the-ordinary features. New signal patterns produce distinctive changes in hitherto unused molecules or sections of molecules, changes representing new information.

There is an apparent catch to this theory. The sort of molecules which might serve as memory traces may have relatively brief life-spans. Since the original traces representing childhood experiences must have vanished long, long ago, how can we explain the persistence of memory? A possible answer is that these molecules leave offspring— and the offspring have the same coded markings or information as their parents. In other words, memory traces make duplicates or "carbon copies" of themselves. The original traces of your earliest memories disappeared in about a week or so, which means that their descendants have been "breeding" in your head at a rate of about fifty generations a year. Contemporary molecules which record events that happened, say, thirty years ago have a pedigree that dates back through some fifteen hundred of their generations.

Memory traces reproduce with a high degree of accuracy, and our recollections are correspondingly reliable. But the process is by no means infallible. When traces fail to breed true, the result is "misprints" and "errata," somewhat garbled information—the equivalent of mutations among heredity-transmitting genes. We may have false memories, recalling details that never existed or entire events that never took place. The testimony of eyewitnesses is notoriously conflicting, and criminal lawyers owe their living to the fact that the duplicated images of memory traces may not be perfectly faithful images.

It should be emphasized that all this is speculation. There is no experimental evidence that memory traces are molecules, self-reproducing or otherwise. On the other hand, investigators in all branches of the life sciences are exploring increasingly at the molecular level, and think along such lines in their efforts to account for the workings of memory—and for its uses. The brain does not merely store the information pouring into it from sense organs: it goes to work on the information. It is continually examining and analyzing. It must have some ingenious and elaborate way of classifying, some system of filing things under appropriate headings.

Take the sense of sight which provides more than 85 per cent of the brain's information. As soon as we can focus our eyes and as long as we can stay awake, images stream into the brain, at a rate of about ten snapshots a second, ten complex patterns of pulses flashed along the optic nerve. Information about many objects and events is sorted as rapidly as it comes into the brain. Memory traces are stored under various headings: size, color, brightness, texture, and so on. And as experience accumulates, new headings are devised for the expanding files.

A person takes in everything. He sees his hands, the eyes of a friend, a pair of birds, a big rock and a little rock. Each of these things differs widely from the others, and their memory traces are correspondingly different. They seem to have little in common. But at some stage there is an important discovery. The person realizes clearly and for the first time that they share a common property, the property of "twoness." Dissimilar classes, hands and eyes and birds and rocks, overlap in a sense and share something not given by the senses directly—an abstraction, a number. Long ago in prehistory when men knew less and were perhaps less human, it required insight to grasp the notion of number. Now that it comes easy, there are the more and more sophisticated abstractions of higher mathematics. Each new notion is a more inclusive indexing tab, a new constellation of memory traces, a new pattern in the brain.

Experience is a process of seeking patterns, and of discovering and inventing ways to classify things. Machines that recognize letters do in a very crude way what brains do smoothly and routinely. We can see letters, numbers, and other symbols in different forms and sizes and at different angles and still abstract essential pattern or similarities from them, recognizing them for what they are. The notion of shape always involves classification. We have learned to see that a coin and a clock and a tree trunk and a wheel, no matter in what positions they happen to be situated, may all be included under a single heading: they all have *circular* forms. The same pattern-finding processes are at work in solving secret ciphers, analyzing brain waves or radar signals from planets, detecting new evidence in photographs of atom trails or cancer cells—and in solving many related problems, with or without the aid of computers. We are always looking for new similarities to guide our thinking.

The brain also has ways of comparing things. Incoming information is compared with stored information to sort out the familiar from the unfamiliar. But there are far subtler mechanisms at work. Memory traces may be brought from different files and put together in new combinations which we call analogies or models. This is one of the outstanding features of scientific thinking. The Greeks conceived of atoms as little devices equipped with hooks so that they could attach themselves to one another. More than two thousand years later scientists spoke in terms of solid spheroids, billiard balls, and later the atom was visualized as a miniature solar system with planetary electrons revolving around a central nucleus. Today research is concentrated on the nucleus which may be a system of shells or a liquid drop or a "somewhat cloudy crystal ball," depending on whose theory is under consideration.

Many analogies have been suggested for the human brain itself. To scientists of the seventeenth century it was a kind of superclockwork device; from the 1920's to relatively recent times it was a telephone exchange system. Today, of course, the brain is widely discussed as an electronic computer—nerve cells resembling transistors, nerve fibers wires, memory traces magnetic cores, and so on. (It should be noted that we pay the brain the high compliment of always comparing it to the most complicated machines known.) All analogies involve bringing together different kinds of stored information to form new combinations, making models of existing things or things that might exist.

This is typical of the artist's as well as the scientist's approach. Similes and metaphors are analogies as well as models of brains and atoms, although their purposes may differ. Voices "more distant and more solemn than a fading star," a harbor "glassy and black like one of those pools they have in the lobbies of grand hotels," "the eyes go iron," "an amethyst remembrance"—these and all the images of poetry represent patterns created in the search for precise and disciplined expression. Similar but generally less disciplined processes are released under the influence of mescaline, LSD (lysergic acid), and other drugs producing vivid hallucinations.

Image-making or imagination may go completely out of control in major mental diseases. The line between things imagined and actual things may disappear. A patient has a crawling sensation on his skin, and it is not *as if* insects were moving there—he feels and sees insects which no one else can perceive. He is driven by guilt, and the inner voices become outer voices, and he hears them accusing him, calling him names loud and clear over the hospital's loudspeaker system—or he sees the floor of his room heaving up as creatures who would murder him burrow underneath. Even when a man's sanity is not in question, analogy and reality may become confused and we recognize fanaticism in all its forms. There is danger and suffering in the misuse, or the diseased use, of memory traces.

From the standpoint of survival in evolution records of the past serve to guide future action. Watch a sea gull circling in search of food. Suddenly it sees something, folds its wings close to its body, plummets like a rock into the water, and comes up with a fish in its beak. It has made a direct hit on a moving target. It does not fall toward the place where it first sees the fish, but somewhere ahead toward the place where the fish will be by the time the gull hits the water. A striking snake or a leaping tiger predicts the behavior of its prey in a similar fashion.

Such actions indicate another way of analyzing information in the brain, a counting and census-taking and computing type of analysis. Too little is known even to guess at what actually goes on in the cortex and other centers. But it is as if certain events are recorded when they first occur, and then each recurrence is counted to maintain a kind of up-to-date table of frequencies. Then the brain seems to compare past frequencies, and compute the odds for and against coming events. In other words, it performs a complicated statistical analysis to arrive at future courses of action.

A star halfback starting on a long run, for example, moves according to such an analysis. His changes of speed and direction, his feints to the right or left, his twistings as he darts into the clear, represent the most successful tactics selected from the experience of years. In a sense, every single maneuver in the entire run has happened before, although the combination of maneuvers may be unique.

In every brief encounter with every would-be tackler, the halfback knows what the opposing player is going to do. He has tried certain dodges in times past, and has been brought to earth with a thud too often to try them again.

Other dodges have proved somewhat more successful; still others, the most successful of all, are used in special circumstances when the chances of breaking loose seem good. Somehow his brain has figured all this out, arriving at a catalog of evasion tactics most likely to succeed.

The general principles are the same in warfare as in sports, from hand-to-hand fighting to jet pursuits in the air. Things are more complicated on a larger scale, of course. The movements of armies and fleets are based on studies of past campaigns and war games, and such studies require special assistance. External memories, books and charts and tables, contain information too voluminous to store in our heads; external brains, computers, analyze the information far more swiftly than the human brain can.

But military predictions, like efforts to forecast business trends or weather or how people will vote, depend to a large degree on past statistics. Only when the laws behind phenomena have been discovered is it possible to predict on any other basis. The law of gravitation permits precise predictions of the motions of satellites, man-made and natural, and eclipses. The laws of chance ensure that in gambling the house always comes out ahead.

The discovery of laws, the designing of tactics and computers, the making of images, and all other distinctively human faculties are believed to require processes carried out in the cortex. This crumpled and convoluted sheet of cells averages only about a tenth of an inch in thickness and would be about the size of a newspaper page if flattened out. But it is here that the highest thinking goes on. The cortex is primarily a place where sensory signals from many sources come together, where memory traces are classified and arranged in new combinations—and where the final decisions are made which determine our actions and plans for action.

Our capacity for caring also involves the cortex and

probably the front parts in particular, if surgical observations are any indication. Operations which sever the connections between these parts and lower centers, so-called "frontal lobotomies," do not always remove symptoms. A patient operated on for the relief of intractable pain may still feel pain and will say so in a matter-of-fact manner. He will also tell you that the pain does not bother him.

When interviewed shortly after a lobotomy, a schizophrenic woman explained that the nonexistent man who had always been following her was still following her. But she was not frightened any more. In another case surgeons decided to operate on a mentally disturbed lawyer, who would go on occasional binges, get into fights, and damage property. He did about the same thing following his lobotomy, the main difference being that he no longer felt guilty afterward. It is easy to see why such surgery is less popular than it was ten years ago.

For all its importance, however, the cortex is by no means independent of lower centers. The human brain works as a single unified system, and years of research will be required before investigators learn how the system is organized. But one of the most significant features of the brain is already known. As has been emphasized in this and the preceding chapter, it incorporates two basic design principles. Many details of internal nerve-cell structure and many nerve pathways, cell-to-cell connections, are controlled by heredity. Specified in genetic codes as precise as wiring diagrams, they are determined the instant the sperm fertilizes the egg. Subsequent development is a matter of following coded instructions, and the results are relatively fixed and rigid cerebral patterns.

Insects furnish the prime examples of rigidity in the shaping of nervous systems. To a very large extent the activities of bees and ants—forming elaborate societies, communicating with one another by highly organized signals, navigating by sunlight, and so on—are automatic activities. We are familiar with such behavior, and have built analogous capacities into our machines. But it is a mistake to compare brains whose complexity is measured in thousands of nerve cells with our brains which contain billions, and to predict that human societies are evolving toward anthill or beehive "regimentation."

Together with its predetermined structures, the human brain includes structures which experience may shape. These structures are more important in us than in any other species. Their patterns take form as we learn and because we learn—and we must learn. The brain needs information like plants need sunlight, and sops information up at a prodigious rate. It needs to be aroused and challenged by fresh experience or it will suffer, as pointed out by Jay Shurley of the University of Oklahoma Medical Center: "If the brain is to continue to function effectively, and the personality to remain integrated, constant stimuli must be received. And these stimuli . . . must be presented in adequate variety and pattern."

Monotony affects the brain as severely as emotional shock or strain. Studies show that half an hour or so of repetitive effort, mental or physical, is enough to make the mind start wandering. Impaired thinking and emotional instability are common symptoms among persons whose lives are devoted chiefly to assembly-line duties, housework, and other routines. Psychiatrists are well aware of the dangerous effects of boredom among shut-in submarine crews, airplane pilots on long flights, and men at remote and isolated outposts.

And when the world is telling us nothing, when nothing interesting is happening, the brain creates a make-believe world of its own. The imagined things in our daydreams and dreams at night and nightmares are often more real and move us more deeply than reality—and we may react to them as if they were real. Men driving trucks for long distances on turnpikes and superhighways may see strange geometric patterns, giant red spiders, and other apparitions on their windshields, and accidents have been known to occur from frantic attempts to avoid hitting imaginary animals that seemed to be scurrying across the road.

Mental and emotional disorders result from being alone in an impoverished environment. Hallucinations occur frequently among hermits and recluses, shipwrecked sailors, patients in iron lungs, elderly persons with impaired hearing and vision. Some of the most vicious tortures devised by man take advantage of what happens to the brain when it is starving for sensation. It is a rare individual who can withstand solitary confinement without cracking up, and monotony is an essential ingredient of brainwashing. We are designed to flourish best in a world of rich and novel experience. In the words of a man who endured prolonged solitary confinement: "Variety is not the spice of life: it is the very stuff of it."

Variety is practically guaranteed by the unprecedented learning capacity of the human brain. As scientists explore the physical universe, they produce new knowledge and new ideas which stimulate further explorations in a self-feeding, self-propelling process. And the world changes. The land is changing with the coming of bulldozers, with the spreading of superhighways and industrial centers and cities into what were once backwoods, out-of-the-way places. Family and community life are changing; human nature is changing. "No one will live all his life in the world in which he was born," Margaret Mead has commented, "and no one will die in the world in which he worked at maturity."

Education, of course, plays a central part in determining the directions of change. It involves elaborate ways of selecting and organizing information. Parents and educators decide what shall be taught, how it shall be taught, in what order, and by what methods. More and more time is being devoted to research on teaching techniques, to the shaping of schedules, to specifying material presented during every classroom period of every course. The organization of school and college curricula represents a step-by-step spelling out of details of programs of instruction, the "input" programs which will, it is hoped, be preserved in the brain's storehouses of memory.

The programs include selected concepts as well as selected facts. They, rather than the structure of the brain, are responsible for the successes and failures of education. They may convey prejudices, illusions that we know when in fact we do not know, or they may embody the principle that knowledge is a growing thing—and that the nature of our certainties and dogmas is subject to change. History provides ample evidence that different programs can produce different kinds of people and different kinds of behavior. Education is the human way of evolving. Its limits are the limits of the flexible, "learning" portions of the brain, and we have not even begun to approach those limits.

THINKING MACHINES OF THE FUTURE

A NUMBER OF YEARS AGO a leading brain anatomist, Gerhardt von Bonin of the University of Illinois Medical Center, made an interesting mistake. Shown an unidentified diagram, he thought a moment and then guessed that it represented the pattern of nerve cells in a part of the cortex concerned with vision. Actually, it turned out to be the diagram of a man-made rather than a natural structure—the provisional circuit of an electronic computing device designed to recognize the letters of the alphabet.

Investigators are rarely fooled by circuit diagrams, but this story indicates that the similarities between brains and computers may be far from trivial. They both include problem-solving networks which receive inputs, signals in the form of coded electrical pulses, and come up with decisions and answers also represented by coded pulses. They are both highly complex and highly organized mosaics of a sort, made up of many similar and relatively simple parts which serve as memory elements, arithmetic and logical components, and so on.

Furthermore, they are both general-purpose systems

which do a variety of things depending on what programs of instructions they are prepared to follow. They can analyze models, classify information, find patterns or regularities in masses of raw data. Most scientists professionally concerned with nerve-cell and electronic circuitry would agree with a statement made by a man who has thought deeply about such resemblances, Warren McCulloch of M.I.T.'s Research Laboratory of Electronics: "The brain is like a computing machine, but there is no computing machine like the brain."

Perhaps the most significant difference is that the electronic computer is not creative in any basic sense. It does not perform the original thinking which keeps it busy. It does not conceive the models it analyzes or the nature of the patterns it seeks and finds. It must be fed ready-made problems and ready-made purposes. What computers may do in times to come is something else again, and as we shall see, some exceedingly ambitious and imaginative plans are under consideration. In any case, those responsible for designing future machines will not necessarily be guided by the design of the brain.

The brain was not constructed according to engineering principles. It is a strange combination of ancient and recent structures, something like a house built on a prehistoric foundation—with Gothic rooms on the first floor, a colonial-type second floor, and a roof which is partly thatched and partly a mixture of Victorian and modern styles. From the lowest to the highest levels, from brainstem to cortex, nature has retained many structures evolved in primitive creatures and laid down one above the other. Computer engineers do not retain old circuitry; they can start from scratch. They can also replace defective parts, while the units of the brain die and are never replaced.

As far as basic units are concerned, however, engineers would like to match the brain in at least one respect—and their efforts are just beginning to pay off. Present-day calculating machines compare with brains as dinosaurs to mice; future models will be far more compact. Enormous strides are being made in methods of cramming more and more hardware into less and less space. No sooner has one laboratory developed a miniature part or circuit than a rival outdoes it with a still smaller version. It is like the story of the machinist who engraved "How's this?" on the head of a pin and mailed the pin to a fellow craftsman. A week later he received the pin back with an answer spelled out on the head: "Not so hot." The answer was engraved inside the dot over the *i* of "this."

Similar feats are being accomplished in the new and competitive field of microelectronics. Take storage devices as an example. ENIAC's memory, such as it was, required more than 300 vacuum tubes and occupied about as much space as an average office. The memory units in most modern computers, wafer-thin magnetic cores about a twentieth of an inch in diameter, are so small that you could pack nearly a quarter of a million of them inside a single tube. Those quarter million cores can hold several thousand times more information than all ENIAC's tubes combined, or to put it another way, it would take more than 160,000 ENIAC-type tubes to hold the information stored in those cores.

But magnetic cores have already been surpassed. The newest machines have even more compact storage devices. These superminiature elements are manufactured by placing sheets of glass in the upper part of a vacuum chamber, where iron-nickel and other magnetic alloys are turned to vapor at high temperatures. The fumes rise through a "mask," a metal strip with small round holes punched in it, and deposit themselves on the surface of the glass sheet in a kind of polka-dot formation. The process, which was originally developed to cover telescope mirrors with even aluminum coatings, is something like spurting paint through a sieve with a spray gun. You end up with a sheet of regularly spaced, film-thin magnetic dots.

The dots of a so-called "magnetic film" memory unit serve the same purpose as magnetic cores. They can store bits of information, binary 1's or 0's depending on the direction of magnetization. But each film-dot may be only a fiftieth of an inch in diameter and four-millionths of an inch thick, which means it is about ten thousand times smaller than a core. This is comparable to compressing an office file cabinet down to the size of a pillbox. Investigators at M.I.T., Remington Rand, and other places have contributed actively to the development of the new magnetic-film techniques which, among other things, make it possible to insert and extract information from memory units more rapidly.

Magnetic-film memories are something for the near future. Several years may pass before they come into extensive use. Looking further ahead, the ultimate size of storage devices seems to be limited only by the sizes of molecules themselves. Individual memory elements may be expected to shrink to microscopic and then to submicroscopic and ultramicroscopic dimensions. Computer experts will be consulting more and more frequently with biologists and physical chemists, taking hints from the design of genetic mechanisms in the nucleus of the cell. It requires no particular gift of foresight to predict synthetic DNA-type molecules, synthetic memory traces for synthetic brains, which carry hundreds of bits of information for every millionth of an inch of their lengths. The problem is whether technology will stop there and, if not, to figure out what the next steps may be.

The trend toward smaller and smaller parts involves all electronic parts, not just memory elements. A flip-flop unit about the size of the *D* on a dime, an amplifier no bigger than your thumbnail, complete adding circuits tiny enough so that three or four would fit comfortably in a teaspoon —these are some of the components under development today. The Burroughs Corporation recently announced work on transistors so small that about a thousand of them could be built into a "module" or circuit block the size of a postage stamp. Of course, nature is still champion in this field. A stamp-size section of the cerebral cortex contains an average of 25 million nerve cells. But that accomplishment does not seem nearly as unattainable as it did a decade ago.

The very notion of individual parts may have to be modified. Engineers are already thinking in terms of molecular regions, regions within the volume of a single crystal which serve special electronic functions. Crystals are grown rather than made, forming under precisely controlled conditions like the snow-and-ice patterns that form on your windowpanes in winter. Tube-replacing transistors, crystals of the metal germanium, are produced in this way. Crystal-making, in the words of one investigator, "has become a highly developed art, like French cooking." The main ingredient may be a pure metal to which you add carefully measured dashes of other chemical elements.

The result is a crystalline block through which electricity may flow. The block is not of uniform composition throughout, but contains different sites so arranged that current passes from one to another along a specified course —a complete circuit built into a jewel. Such crystals can do the work of and replace many conventional components. Using them for computers and other electronic devices is like building a home out of a few prefabricated units instead of thousands of individual parts. Instead of present circuits which produce the timed pulses required in calculating machines, for example, there will be tiny crystals. (These so-called "oscillators," by the way, may also be used in wristwatches of the future—all-electronic timekeepers stamped out in a single operation and containing no moving parts.)

Another coming feature is a thin-film circuit designed to operate at extremely low temperatures. Under ordinary conditions you need voltage supplied by a battery or generator to keep current flowing, the voltage being analogous to the head of pressure which maintains water flow in pipes. But at temperatures down around absolute zero metals acquire an amazing property. They become "superconductive"; that is, their resistance to the flow of current vanishes. Once a current is set up in a metal ring it will move in merry-go-round circles indefinitely, without any source of voltage to drive it. This is roughly equivalent to making a car with frictionless wheels, a motorless car which, after an initial push, rolls along on its own forever or until you apply the brakes.

Investigators have developed ways of depositing not merely metallic memory dots on glass sheets but entire circuits. They have also developed microrefrigerators, liquid-helium chambers in which the temperature is about 450 degrees below zero Fahrenheit. By combining these devices it is possible to construct all kinds of low-power electronic switches and other units. For example, a current could be kept flowing in a superconductive metal strip and might represent a bit of information, a memory trace. To stop the current, to erase the stored information, you apply a magnetic field—and when the field is turned off, a low-voltage "push" would restore the flow. Since the off-on cycles can be used to do counting, similar strips serve as adding as well as storage devices.

At the present rate of progress it would be foolhardy to guess how far engineers will go and how soon. About two years ago Richard Feynman, a leading physicist at the California Institute of Technology in Pasadena, gave a talk about the future possibilities of doing things on a small scale. Among other things, he spoke about awarding $1,000 to the first person making "a rotating electric motor which can be controlled from the outside and, not counting lead-in wires, is only a $\frac{1}{64}$-inch cube"—a cube each side of which is shorter than the spaces between the letters in the words of this sentence.

This was more of an expressed intention than an official offer. But one of Feynman's fellow citizens of Pasadena, William McLennan of Electro-Optical Systems, took up the challenge in earnest. Using a watchmaker's lathe and a microscope, he succeeded in building a motor which meets the above specifications. It has thirteen parts and weighs about a hundred thousandth of an ounce. Feynman lived up to his part of the bargain by mailing McLennan a check for $1,000. The machine could represent more than a stunt. It might turn out to be the hint of an "invisible" industry, the forerunner of micromotors which will be used to manufacture microelectronic devices on microassembly lines.

Why make parts smaller and smaller? The chief pressure nowadays comes from the Defense Department and other agencies concerned with national security. Miniature and subminiature parts are lightweight parts, and military planners are willing to pay a high price for savings along these lines. Reduce the weight of the electronic device in a rocket by 1 pound, and you reduce the rocket's take-off weight by 100 pounds—and this 100 to 1 ratio is of critical importance in the design of guided missiles, satellite launchers, and space ships of all sorts. Such considerations apply to bombers and other large aircraft, which may contain fifty or more times as many electronic components as World War II models.

But reducing weight is not the whole story. It is just as important to get more for the same weight. As tactics

Miniature electronic circuits such as these, designed by Burroughs engineers, indicate the trend toward smaller and smaller computers.

and strategies become increasingly complex, computers must also become more complex. They are called on to handle more difficult problems, which means more elaborate circuitry and more parts. For example, take mobile "intelligence" or deciphering devices for use in combat areas. You want them to solve intricate ciphers without adding to their weight, so there is a constant race between the men who conceive new ciphers and the men who make electronic components. Another advantage is that small parts often tend to be more reliable.

Speed is also a significant factor. The direction of the magnetic field in a thin-film dot can be reversed faster than the field in a core, so that you can extract or store information faster. Furthermore, you can save time because of the simple fact that smaller parts may be put closer together. If two parts are separated by 1 foot, an electrical signal moving at the speed of light takes about a billionth of a second to negotiate the distance between them. Now it may not seem like much of an improvement to decrease that time by decreasing the distance to, say, a hundredth of a foot. But when you take into account how many signals and how many different channels are involved, the difference can be significant.

An analogous situation would be to make a road shorter between two neighboring towns. Eliminating a few curves might reduce the driving time by only a few minutes or so. But if you add up the time saved after thousands of round trips, the total may amount to many man-years—and similar savings are made by using tiny electronic circuits. It is a matter of shifting your perspective. A second is an enormous stretch of time in the superfast world of computer activities, where things happen at rates which we cannot comprehend and operations will be measured in billionths of a second.

Greater speed, attained with small-scale parts and other improvements, will help considerably in handling the most time-consuming research problems. If you are studying the possibility of making accurate weather forecasts a month in advance, for example, the equations that must be solved may involve some 100 billion multiplications of ten-digit decimal numbers. No one would think of using a machine like ENIAC for the task, because it would take 30,000 years to arrive at a one-month forecast. IBM's STRETCH could do the work in a bit more than three weeks, which brings the problem within a reasonable range. Machines of the not-too-distant future will be at least ten times faster, which brings the time down to about two days.

These machines will include more than microminiature parts. For example, take the FX-1, which has been developed under the leadership of William Papian, head of the Digital Computers Group at M.I.T.'s Lincoln Laboratory. The FX-1, which just started operating this summer, is the first general-purpose computer with an all-magnetic-film memory. But even more significant, it has extra-fast pulse circuits which depend on the use of special new transistors. The signal traffic inside the FX-1 system moves faster than ever before, and many of its features will be incorporated into the commercial computers of the future. Furthermore, an FX-2 is already in the planning stage.

But one thing must be remembered as far as highly publicized advances in microelectronics are concerned. Small parts by themselves will not raise the "IQ level" of a computer. The big job still falls on those who tell it what to do, who prepare orders for it to follow. A machine's capabilities, like a child's, depend on the quality of its instructions—and the future is certain to see revolutionary developments in programming. At present you must describe every procedure required for a computer to solve a problem. You must give it a complete set of elementary instructions.

We speak loosely about computers answering questions, but that is not actually what happens. When you get right down to it, today's computers do not answer questions. They follow long series of instructions leading to answers, which is something quite different. To illustrate the difference, imagine that an executive has a mindless secretary who can only follow similar instructions, and he wants to know whether his files contain a letter from John A. Smith dated February 4, 1961. He writes out the instructions: go to the file cabinet nearest the window in my office; pull out the second drawer from the top; take out the "S" folder; go through the letters until you reach those from people whose last names start with "Sm . . . ," then "Smi . . . ," and so on to "Smith"; find the "John A. Smith" letters; and select the one with the date February 4, 1961.

Fortunately for the cause of sanity and business efficiency, a real-life secretary responds meaningfully to a question: "Do we have a letter dated February 4, 1961, from John A. Smith?" She does not need a step-by-step program. She has a different sort of program based on experience, a program which consists of a general course of action rather than a painfully detailed set of actions.

There is reason to believe that similarly generalized programs will ultimately be prepared for computers, that scientists will be able to ask genuine questions instead of spelling out long-winded procedures for getting answers. Now they must tell the machines to go to memory location A, follow the instructions stored there, go to memory location B and follow those instructions, and so on through hundreds or thousands of instructions. Tomorrow they may simply say: "What is the solution to this equation?"

A group of Lincoln Laboratory investigators is working on a unique question-answering program. The study should be of interest to baseball fans, because a computer will have its memory filled with information about the locations, dates, and scores of all games played during one American League season. It will answer thousands of questions, simple ones like "What team won in New York on July 5?" and more complicated ones like "How many times did the Red Sox lose by a run two days after the Yankees beat the Indians by a run?" The replies will be brief and to the point: "yes," "no," "twenty," "no game," "one run," and so on.

The program will also enable the machine to respond to "noisy" questions, questions whose meanings are not clear. It will recognize the ambiguity of an inquiry such as the following: "Which team won the most games in July?" This question may seem fairly simple, but a moment's consideration will reveal that it has a number of possible interpretations. Among other things, it can mean "Of all teams, which team won the most games in July?" or "Which team won more of all its scheduled games in

July than in any other month?" Confronted with such vagaries, the computer will ask a question of its own: "What do you mean?" It will continue asking until you prepare a reworded and unambiguous question.

If the experiment works as expected, and results should be known within a year, the way will be clear for programs involving more complicated questions and more crucial information stored in more voluminous memories. For example, sufficiently knowledgeable computers would be helpful at information booths in railroad and airline terminals, department stores, tourist centers, and convention halls. In libraries they might replace almanacs, *Who's Who* volumes, handbooks, and other reference works, or serve as automatic file-searchers in offices. Instead of analyzing charts and other experimental records, scientists could feed research results into an appropriately programmed computer and ask a few pointed questions.

Of course, such machines do not shine at conversation. They give terse answers, and when a question is unclear, they can only keep asking for a better question. Things would proceed more smoothly if a computer could indicate what the trouble is and perhaps suggest improved wordings. Working with such a computer would be something like playing tennis with a player worthy of your mettle; working with present-day computers is more like batting a tennis ball against a wall. Your problems come back at you rapidly, but you learn little about improving tactics and strategies and the finer points of the subtle game of problem-solving.

Consider how an investigator works when he tackles a difficult new problem. He does not always know exactly what he wants to find out. His first question may be a general one, and later questions become more specific as he learns more. He may not be fully aware of the limitations and potentialities of his data, or of the sort of new data he needs to attain his objectives. He may learn by consulting modern computers. But each step in the learning process requires taking time to write out a new program and waiting while the machine computes an answer before going to the next phase and another new program.

So research is under way at several laboratories to develop rapid, two-way communications between men and machines. Of course, actual spoken conversation will not be possible until listening devices which can recognize speech and talking devices which can utter words are developed. Although such devices are being studied, they may not be available for ten years or so. Unspoken communications are also difficult, "conversations" during which the investigator will write out remarks and the machine will respond with various types of replies.

The writing may be done with something like the so-called "light pen." This device is a "slender metal tube with a glass eye," a lens through which light passes from a bright spot on a cathode-ray screen. It is equipped with a light-detecting photoelectric cell. When it is placed close to the screen of an appropriately programmed machine and moved over the surface, the spot follows and leaves a glowing trail. Originally developed as a pistol-shaped device for use with the Air Force's SAGE defense system, it can be used to write sentences on the screen—and some day machines will be able to read the sentences and type or write sentences of their own.

Communications need not be carried out with sentences only. To computers as well as to human beings, a picture may be worth a thousand words. When two engineers are talking over a new design—say, for a jet motor or a computer—they make rough sketches and graphs. Substitute a computer for one of the engineers and you will have an idea of the shape of things to come. Designers will express their plans by drawing diagrams on television-type screens,

Heinrich Ernst gives instructions to computer-controlled hand (background). The hand, originally designed by the American Machine & Foundry Company to handle "hot" radioactive materials, has been modified to include special electronic sense organs.

and computers will make suggestions and tactful criticisms. Experimental programs for such discussions are already being tested.

Also, the fundamental nature of computer networks may be expected to change radically in the more remote future. Some of the changes will make the machines more "cerebral," more human in their circuitry or internal structure as well as in their accomplishments. To be sure, very little is known about the higher workings of the brain. But they certainly depend on intricate nerve-cell networks —and the cells are interconnected in ways that differ widely from those specified in the wiring diagrams for computers.

These differences may help account for the fact that brains seem to operate relatively simply in doing things which machines can do only on the basis of considerable amounts of stored information and programs containing thousands of instructions. The machines operate chiefly by brute-force tactics.

Two pattern-recognition projects using the TX-2 computer indicate the sort of improvements that may be possible. One of the projects has already been described in Chapter 5. The computer is programmed to recognize hand-printed letters of the alphabet by a complicated and detailed procedure. Every letter is examined for twenty-eight characteristics—the number of horizontal lines, the number of vertical lines, the presence and locations of unenclosed spaces, and so on. Then different letters are compared for each one of the different characteristics and identified accordingly. This system works, but it works slowly. Furthermore, it recognizes only ten letters, and it would require far more time and circuitry to identify the whole alphabet.

The second project involves the same objective, but a different system. Imagine a device designed to recognize four and only four letters—say, A, O, X, and E. It has a reading unit consisting of a mosaic of sixty-four light-sensitive phototubes, and when the image of a letter registers on the mosaic, the affected phototubes respond by producing signals representing the patterns they "see." The mosaic is divided into sixteen 4-tube blocks, each being wired to a separate information-analyzing unit which receives all the signals from its phototube block. That gives us an array of sixteen analyzers handling data from different areas of the mosaic.

There is one more step in the system. The analyzers in turn are wired to a second array made up of only four special units. These units are the executive elements. Provided with information from the other elements of the device, they have the final say-so when it comes to identifying the observed letter. The wiring is arranged in such a way that if the combined signal patterns from the analyzers represent the letter X, only the X unit in the last array will fire. So when one of the four decision-making units emits a signal, it is in effect naming one of the four letters which the device is designed to recognize.

This is a simplified version of a system which is actually being tested on the TX-0 and TX-2 computers by Lawrence Roberts of the M.I.T. Lincoln Laboratory. The program he prepared describes a mosaic of about 1,300 instead of 64 phototubes, an array of 288 analyzers instead of 16, and a second array of 44 instead of 4 executive units. In other words, he has programmed the machine to recognize as many as 44 characters. Furthermore, he includes a reward feature so that the machine receives a reinforcing or "encouraging" signal every time it makes a correct identification during its learning period.

Here is what you might do if you wanted to train the machine. You could start communicating with it by using a light pen and drawing a first letter, say A, on a screen. The TX-2 sees the letter, hesitates a moment, and then flashes a letter on the screen. The letter will probably not be an A, and if it is, it will just be a lucky guess. If some other letter flashes on the screen, you operate a switch which in effect tells the machine that the pattern was an A. Then you show the machine letters in a long random list which includes all the letters of the alphabet and also different ways of writing the letters, pressing a reward button every time it makes a correct response.

Under equivalent conditions a computer using Roberts' program will learn to identify the letters correctly 94 per cent of the time after about forty trials for each letter. Then you could go through the numbers 0 to 9, which gives the machine a reading vocabulary of thirty-six characters, or just eight short of its full capacity. The program which makes all this possible, known as Adapt II, contains only 200 instructions and enables the machine to process characters at a rate of four a second. These experiments are part of a series which started with the study of a learning system resembling that developed by Frank Rosenblatt of the Cornell Aeronautical Laboratory in Buffalo and called the "Perceptron." But Roberts' program differs radically from that of the original Perceptron.

Brain investigators are particularly interested in Roberts' project, because it represents a device resembling the brain in certain important respects. The image-registering mosaic, of course, is a kind of sense organ. The 1,300 phototubes in it may be regarded as electronic versions of the light-sensitive cells in the retina of the eye. The analyzing and executive units correspond to nerve cells, and the arrays in which they are arranged correspond to nerve-cell layers in that part of the cortex concerned with vision. Indeed, there is reason to believe that the data-processing circuits in the highest centers of the brain involve a hierarchy with many sensing elements and fewer analyzing elements and, at the top of the pyramid, still fewer decision-making or executive elements. Information seems to be sorted, filtered, and condensed on its way from sense organs to cortex.

In any case, it is clear that at least some of our most ingenious devices will have circuitry increasingly like the brain's. It is also clear that this trend will be accelerated as we know the brain better and better. New discoveries about the organization and functions of the 10 billion cells in the cortex, for example, will certainly guide those scientists involved in continuing efforts to explore the potentialities of computers to the fullest. The checker-playing machine that has not yet attained champion status simply because funds are not available for its "education" is one example of the fact that automatic learners have already arrived on the scene.

But will machines ever learn in the ultimate sense? Will they write their own programs, develop improved recognition and translating systems, find new patterns and new analogies and new models? Will they be able to organize themselves, to evolve and become an electronic species in their own right? These are difficult goals, but there is no evidence that any one of them is unattainable. The tantalizing aspect of the computer story is the part that cannot be told, because certain developments cannot be predicted. Judging by the past, however, these developments will revolutionize our ways of thinking and doing things.

The design of future machines will benefit from the findings of brain investigators, and the reverse also holds true. Brain investigators will consult with computer specialists to gain insight into the workings of the nervous system. The use of computers to simulate nerve-cell networks is just beginning, and if the machines can run models of floods and stars and political systems, you can be sure that sooner or later they will deal with models of brains and human beings. They represent the most powerful tools yet developed for the study of human behavior. Many psychologists use terms like "input-output devices," "storage units," "data-processing," "programming," and other phrases borrowed from the vocabulary of computer experts in describing their problems.

Computers will also find wide application in helping us to train our brains more effectively. They will serve as teaching aids, and it is only a matter of time before they will be at work in every large school. Even ignoring the fact that teacher shortages will become more critical, the situation is bad enough right now. For one thing, teachers can rarely provide the degree of individual attention which their pupils need. They are far too busy heeding the bells that signal the end of one class period and the beginning of the next—and trying to impart required amounts of information to classes of as many as forty or more students.

Some day much of the information will be imparted with the assistance of computers. Teaching machines already exist which present material to students, ask questions about the material, and check the answers. Moreover, some machines do not present the material in the same order to every student. The order depends on the answers of the individual student, and if he happens to have difficulty grasping certain ideas, he will be confronted with additional information and questions.

Now think of a computer connected with twenty or thirty such machines, each working with a different student. It can monitor the entire situation. It can receive information about the progress of all the students, analyze and compare records, and evaluate the effectiveness of different ways of presenting information. It can bring learning problems to the attention of the teacher, who will have time for individuals requiring special help. Routines are as much of a burden to teachers as to other workers, and machines will play a major role in classrooms of the future.

Computers have already entered the factory. All major aircraft companies use milling machines which operate according to principles originally worked out at M.I.T. Spinning bits move along complex pathways in space as they cut through solid metal under the guidance of computers following instructions written on reels of tape—and turn out parts with tricky contours such as turbine buckets, wing and missile panels, and rib structures. For example, take the Convair F106, a supersonic fighter-interceptor plane which has more than 50,000 different parts in its air frame alone. These parts include twenty to thirty odd-shaped doors, and all of them are automatically cut out of a huge aluminum plate more than an inch thick, 8 feet wide, and 24 feet long.

More elaborate machines are coming. Heinrich Ernst of M.I.T., following a suggestion of Claude Shannon and Marvin Minsky, is working on a computer-controlled hand which has a pair of grasping tongs serving as fingers and is covered with a "skin" of plastic. Imbedded in the skin of each finger are fourteen electric organs sensitive to touch and two photocell eyes so that the hand can see where it is going. If you tell a computer to pick up an object and drop it in a nearby wastebasket, it will manipulate the hand accordingly.

The linking of artificial brains and artificial hands represents a gradual but inevitable development which is of major concern to labor, management, and government. We have heard a good deal about technological unemployment and other serious consequences of introducing automation too rapidly. But much can also be said on the positive side. In times of nostalgia we may look back to less complicated days and regret the passing of the family spinning wheel and butter churn and the blacksmith's forge. But it is difficult to romanticize the assembly line. There is certainly nothing to regret about the eventual passing of this institution, assuming that the changeover is planned as carefully as the electronic devices which make it possible.

The scope of what is happening in all fields, accelerating change further accelerated by the coming of computers, must be considered against a broad background. All this is part of a process that started at least 2 or 3 billion years ago when living things somehow arose out of sunlight, water, and dissolved minerals and crystals and gases. Ever since then animate matter has been organizing itself into more and more elaborate forms, increasingly complex species among which man is the latest and most complex.

The rise of computers has been called a Second Industrial Revolution, but it is far more than that. It is the mark of human development, a sign that our kind of evolution is just beginning. We are uniquely designed to obtain and analyze information, and not only the ready-made information accessible to our natural sense organs and to the sense organs of other species. We go after new information, and all that we have discovered to date is nothing compared to what we shall discover

All our past explorations are merely practice for explorations yet to come, like a baby crawling before it walks. Our skies will soon be filled with satellites: flying telephone and television receiver-transmitters, flying telescopes, flying radar and radio astronomy stations, flying laboratories and launching platforms. Every device will be recording enormous quantities of information to help us build extensive communication networks for growing populations —and vehicles for ventures into interplanetary space. We need machines to help us make sense of this flood of new information.

The evolution of all other living things has depended on changes in their bodies. But man could evolve indefinitely without any such changes, with the same brain he has now. Our kind of evolution depends on cultural changes, on what we learn, on the things we build. In a basic sense, human evolution *is* the evolution of machines, and of these, computers are the most significant. Perhaps more than anything else, the design of artificial-intelligence systems will determine our future as a species.